MONKEYS OF THE MESQUITE

The Social Life of the South Texas Snow Monkey

ðŸ‚ ðŸ‚ ðŸ‚

Mary McDonald Pavelka
University of Calgary

KENDALL/HUNT PUBLISHING COMPANY
4050 Westmark Drive   Dubuque, Iowa 52002

Lou Griffin has kept the Arashiyama West colony together for more than a decade. This is a job which does not afford her the luxury of time to write about the animals that she knows best. This book is dedicated to her efforts. All proceeds from the sale of this book will go directly to the daily maintenance of the colony.

Snow Monkeys in Texas.

Cover and interior photos by Karen Dickey

Printed in the United States of America
10 9 8 7 6 5 4 3 2

CONTENTS

Foreword

ૐ ૐ ૐ

Linda Marie Fedigan
Department of Anthropology
University of Alberta
Edmonton, Alberta, Canada T6G 2H4

Many primatologists are anthropologists who have taken or taught introductory sociocultural anthropology courses in which ethnographies are a god-
send. Ethnographies are short, readable monographs that describe the social and
cultural lives of a group of people in an accessible and entertaining manner. For
the beginning student or interested novice, ethnographies provide welcome
relief from the mental gymnastics of trying to comprehend the kinship structure,
marriage rules, or linguistic practices of another culture. An ethnography is a
good read that gives the non-specialist a type of affinity with the group of people
under study, and insight into them, that would not be possible from sophisticated analyses of summarized data. Ethnograhies make the science and the
people come alive.

Mary Pavelka set out to provide a similar learning tool for students of
primatology—a short, descriptive account of the lives of one group of monkeys,
the Japanese macaques of south Texas. Oddly enough, there are very few such
descriptive accounts of one species, or one group, available in primatology as
compared to cultural anthropology, However, *Monkeys of the Mesquite* does
follow in the writing tradition of books such as *Almost Human* by Shirley Strum
and *Peacemaking Among Primates* by Frans de Waal. All are much needed
books for those of us who teach a science that is highly quantified and examines
little known animals to test complex theories from evolutionary biology.

There is an inherent danger for the scientists who try to make their work
accessible by describing it in a "story" format. Some scientists are offended by
the notion that our life's work can be told in the form of stories, or narratives,
and believe that such an attempt will damage our reputation as objective,
rigorous researchers. However, those scholars who study the practice of science
itself, tell us that almost all scientific ideas and theories are essentially stories,
that is, they are created by piecing together an organized and plausible sequence
of events that is intuitively satisfying while at the same time following rigorous,
standardized rules. These same science-studies scholars inform us that storytel-
ling itself is one of the defining human traits, that our need for causal and

chronological connection makes us who we are. Every group of humans ever studied shares stories that help to define them, from origin myths to the gossip about what their neighbors did last week. Primatologists at rest tell each other stories about their animals all the time.

But in public, and in print, we scientists usually hide our stories under an armor of specialized language and structural rules of presentation, such that only an expert can decode them. We are always in need of people who can tell scientific stories in ways accessible to a general audience without distorting the expert's perception of the subject matter. To make this translation from scientific "speak" to public understanding is not an easy task, it requires a gift, a skill that is possessed by the author of this book.

As Mary was writing this "primatography," she sent me chapter after chapter to read for what she called "the cringe factor." How many scientists have not cringed when they read a passage in a newspaper or popular journal describing scientific work with which they are familiar? We cringe when we realize that some beautiful, complex, intricate aspect of nature has been grossly oversimplified and indeed sacrificed to produce a catchy headline or a cute angle that the popular writer thinks will resonate with the public. This practice not only annoys the expert, it demeans the reader by assuming that they are not capable of understanding and appreciating the "true story." Suffice it to say that *Monkeys of the Mesquite* does not make a primatologist cringe in order to provide entertaining reading for the non-specialist. Even the experts will learn from and enjoy reading this book. And it does provide the truly fascinating story of the individuals, interactions and events that have made up the history of the Arashiyama West group of Japanese monkeys, stripped clean of the apparatus of authentication—data tables, statistical tests, voluminous citations—that can all be found elsewhere and that only obscure the story for the student and the interested public.

This is one of the books that I assign to the students in my introductory primatology classes, and I also give copies to my friends and relatives who want to find out what it is really like to be a primatologist and to know another species intimately. My students rave about the book, many ask me how they could get to meet these monkeys, and some go on to become primatologists. And, after 25 years of politely accepting copies of my scientific articles and books, my parents read Mary Pavelka's book, and seemed to finally understand what I do and why I have such a passion for studying monkeys. I can think of no more fitting accolade to confer on this book than to affirm that it effectively communicates to our students and to the public at large why our primate relatives are so deserving of our attention and worthy of our consideration. Read it, you will enjoy it.

PREFACE

ଶ୍ଧ   ଶ୍ଧ   ଶ୍ଧ

Since 1981 I have studied the social behaviour of the Arashiyama West colony of Japanese macaques. In that time I have come to know the individual animals well and have developed a good understanding of Japanese monkey society. My first-hand experience observing the social behaviour and dynamics of Japanese macaques has been of great value to me in teaching primate behaviour. Richly detailed descriptions of the social life of the animals that I know first-hand help students to get a sense of what monkeys are really like, of how complex and intricate are their social dynamics, and of how similar and dissimilar they are to humans and other primates. This book is intended to provide this description in the form of a supplementary text for students in primate behaviour courses.

It is valuable for students to come away from a primate behaviour course with detailed knowledge of the social life of at least one species. Commonly, Introduction to Social and Cultural Anthropology courses require at least two books: a course textbook which covers a range of topics and explores general principles of society, culture, and cross-cultural variation, and a supplementary book, a case study which describes in much greater detail one society. As a student, and later when I taught such a course myself, I found this format to be useful. Many books exist for those teaching Social and Cultural Anthropology—the Spindler series alone includes almost 100 volumes. However in primate behaviour, short, descriptive overviews of specific societies are not common. This book then, is the primate behaviour equivalent to the case studies used in social and cultural anthropology—a "primatography" if you will.

While I do engage in the occasional speculation or theoretical musing, I have tried to keep the material descriptive, reporting behaviour as I have seen it. In some instances I raise questions without answering them—I leave it to readers and instructors to think about both proximate and ultimate explanations. The book is intended to be quick and easy reading for students new to primate behaviour, and I have tried to keep it short. I hope that it provides food for thought and material for discussion among more senior readers. The occasional anecdote about the experience of doing fieldwork on monkeys in Texas is included, as are some descriptions of human-monkey interactions. All reveal something about primate behaviour.

The book is written in a popular, hopefully accessible style—the same style that observers use when talking among themselves. I am attempting to convey to the reader the full picture that I have in my mind, to convey the richness of my own observations. This could not be achieved with the objective scientific writing style of journal articles. In this book I often use the human term which will best describe what I think is going on in a given social interaction, or what best describes an individual animal. I did not approach the study of these animals from the point of view that they would be like humans and that human terms would best describe their behaviour—the descriptions in this book are based on observations over a period of 12 years, including several hundred hours of systematic data collection followed by quantitative analysis. I hope that one or two students may become interested enough after reading a popular description such as this to go out and rigorously test some of the hypotheses. For those who might take issue with the style, I hope the book will be useful for discussion of anthropomorphism, objectivity, and related topics.

Various people have provided me with encouragement and/or specific feedback on drafts of this work, and this support has been crucial to the successful completion of the manuscript. First and foremost among these is my husband, Joe Pavelka. Very special thanks to Lou Griffin and Linda Fedigan for answering my endless questions, giving feedback on drafts of the manuscript, and providing encouragement and support. Also, I wish to thank Pamela Asquith, Annie Katzenberg, Nancy Copping, Shelagh Hamer Wrazej and Mary Ann Morel. Some of my students were kind enough to volunteer their time to give me feedback from a student's perspective—for this I thank Margo Schulte, Sherry Norman, and Sashie Tillekeratne. Tracy Marie Wyman provided the map of the site.

Snow Monkeys in South Texas

Sitting in the hot sun, I wondered how I could possibly go back to Canada and start law school as planned. A young monkey mother sat grooming her infant in the shade of a thorny acacia bush, ever watchful of a much higher-ranking family group nearby. A horned toad lizard scurried past in the dust, arousing the interest of a juvenile monkey play group which followed it into the bushes. Nearby there was a splash as two other juveniles jumped together into the pond. Doves and scissortail flycatchers swooped overhead. Off in the distance some monkeys were fighting; I could hear their vocalisations—so could the young mother, who looked nervously in the direction of the sounds. The higher-ranking group was nonchalant, unconcerned. The air was hot and smelled of dust and animals.

It was May, 1981. I was a student in a field school on the techniques of studying nonhuman primate behaviour taught by Linda and Larry Fedigan. With nine other students, I had travelled to Dilley, Texas where we would come to know the Arashiyama West colony of Japanese snow monkeys. Snow monkeys in Texas? It is a long story.

BRIEF HISTORY OF THE COLONY ❧

In the early 1950's, Japanese scientists began feeding a wild troop of Japanese monkeys in a mountainous region known as Arashiyama not far from the city of Kyoto. The feeding was intended to keep the animals within view long enough that individual animals could be identified, and accurate counts could be obtained. In 1966 this troop had grown to 163 animals and fissioned into two smaller groups. These troops were named Arashiyama A and B. The A troop extended their range into the suburbs of the city of Kyoto, where they became a nuisance. In 1972, after a six year search for a new home, the entire Arashiyama A troop was transported to Encinal, Texas, where it would thrive in the arid brush country of south Texas. Their new home was just north of the American/Mexican border town of Laredo/Nuevo Laredo. The desert-like environment, very different from the mountainous home from which the monkeys had come, provided the opportunity to observe adaptation in action.

1

My involvement with these monkeys began in 1981, one year after the animals had been relocated again to a ranch about 95 kilometres north of Encinal, near the town of Dilley. Dilley is on Interstate 35, about halfway between San Antonio and Laredo. From Dilley it is five kilometres to the locked gates of the private family ranch, then another 16 kilometres along a dirt road inside the ranch to the site of the South Texas Primate Observatory. Initially the site included three house trailers for researchers just outside of the compound. The compound was an area of 20 hectares enclosed by a three metre high electrified fence. At the time of this move the troop came to be known as the Arashiyama West. Although the term "snow monkey" is only appropriate for some of Japan's northernmost monkey troops, in popular usage all Japanese monkeys are often referred to by this term. In hot dry south Texas, amid thorny cactus, mesquite, and acacia, a troop of snow monkeys thrives.

Both of the homes that the snow monkeys have had in Texas have been located through Dr. Claude Bramblett, a professor at the University of Texas in Austin who discussed the troop and its history with his classes. Lou Griffin, a graduate student in the late 1970's when the search was underway for the second home, was instrumental in securing the current site. Lou herself became the next on-site manager, taking care of daily management while working on her dissertation. Thirteen years later she continues to work full-time as on-site manager and director of the facility.[1]

CURRENT CONDITIONS   ✍

Within the enclosure is a large cleared field with a dense brush line and creekbed running the length of it. At the south end are two large ponds, used by the monkeys for drinking and swimming. The area around the water is also covered in brush—primarily mesquite and chaparral. The fields that extend east and west of the creekbed are planted each spring with various crops on which the monkeys forage. Although the fence does not truly contain the animals, the area within the enclosure is their home, and most are not interested in leaving it. Over the decade that the monkeys have been at the Dilley site, they have changed the limits of their home range. Always responsive to changes in available resources, they have, over time, learned to utilise some of the shade and natural forage outside of the enclosed area. But for the most part, the area within the enclosure is where daily activities take place. If the enclosed area is the home range, then the creekbed and the ponds are the core areas within this range, as the animals spend the vast majority of their time in these areas. It is in this area with cover, shade, reduced visibility, and water that the animals tend to rest and socialise. The fields are utilised primarily for temporary foraging

---

1   Management of the troop will be discussed in more detail in chapter 8.

South Texas Primate Observatory

Chow line

People Gate

Main gate

Road to town

KEY

▨	Mesquite-brush
●	Water source
■	Storage
⊞	Caging
XX	Climbing structure
—	Colony fence
····	Barbed Wire

The monkeys in south Texas spend a good deal of the hot Texas day in the shade or in the water.

Central adult male sitting on a wagon wheel.

Adult male with cheek pouches full.

forays, and often the animals will return to the core area to sit and eat what they have stored up in their cheek pouches.

The research value of these monkeys derives from the fact that they are known as individuals, and have been studied from birth. The provisioning that made this possible has been continued in Texas, but otherwise this naturally formed intact group continue to live as wild animals, roaming freely over the 20 hectares. Apart from sporadic trapping for the purpose of tattooing and medical intervention, they exist with a minimum of human intervention, but are habituated to the presence of at least one behavioural observer. A small group of African vervet monkeys, *Cercopithecus aethiops*, now share the area with the macaques.[2]

Possibly, the monkeys would be able to live off the land without being provided extra food; however, the 20 hectare enclosure was never large enough for this. Within two years the monkeys had eaten every cactus in the area, and had stripped clean the mesquite trees. Mesquite, while a barbecue favourite, is actually a nuisance plant that has taken over much of south Texas, and getting rid of it is nearly impossible. Local ranchers, on seeing how this troop of monkeys destroy mesquite, often joke that they would like to "borrow" the troop. The monkeys are fed in the least disruptive manner possible. Grain, such as corn and milo, as well as monkey chow and cattle cubes are scattered along the roadway within the enclosure. This scattering of food is intended to simulate

---

2   Further reference will be made to the vervet monkeys later in the book.

Water on chowline after a heavy rain.

a more natural distribution of food resources, and to avoid the aggression that would come with providing food from one or two specific locations. Once or twice a week, they also receive a truckload of produce brought down from San Antonio by volunteer Kay McMichael Trevino.

Each of the monkeys is marked with a facial and a leg tattoo for identification purposes. At the first Texas site, in Encinal, a large permanent capture structure enabled the researchers and managers to hold one massive trap each year for the purpose of tattooing the latest birth cohort. At the Dilley site, the capture structure was intended to be built after the move, but funding for the structure did not come through. Trapping is now done sporadically, with small box traps. This method, while very labour intensive and considerably less effective at ensuring that all babies get tattoos, is usually less disruptive to the monkeys than would be a large trapping of the whole troop. After a monkey is trapped, it is quickly sedated, tattooed, weighed, measured, examined and, once fully awake, released. The ordeal is over later the same day.

Observation conditions for researchers are excellent at this site. The animals are wild, uncaged, and living freely within a naturally intact social group. But unlike wild troops, these animals can always be found and observed, and extensive information about each individual animal is available. For many observational study projects, this situation combines the best of wild and captive study sites. The monkeys normally ignore the one or two humans who wander among them, and thus it is possible to observe closely the intricate complexities of their social life.

The electrified fence has never been able to completely contain the monkeys. They are extremely intelligent and curious animals, with thick pads on their hands and feet that enable them to take electric shocks that would apparently stop a baboon in its tracks.[3] For the first few years the main body of the troop stayed within the enclosed area which contains food, water, shade, and the sleeping trees. It was their home range, and the monkeys seemed to accept the fence as though it were a natural barrier. However, the normal social organisation and life history patterns of Japanese monkeys are such that it was to be expected that some animals would always want out.

JAPANESE MONKEY SOCIAL ORGANISATION ❧

Japanese monkeys live in social groups ranging in size from about 40 individuals in nonprovisioned groups to several hundred individuals in provisioned groups. The core of each troop is comprised of groups of related females and their immature offspring with unrelated adult males. In all primate groups, one or both of the sexes normally disperse from the group into which they were born (the *natal* group) and join other groups. Japanese monkey society is characterised by male dispersal and female philopatry—males leave at puberty to join other groups and females remain in the natal group throughout their lives. Thus the core of the society is related females, and most of the social dynamics are best understood within this context. The social life history of males and females is very different, and much less is known about male life history patterns because of the difficulties of following individual males throughout their lives.

For the Arashiyama West monkeys at the South Texas Primate Observatory, male dispersal presents a problem. Young females stay close to their mother in their adolescent years and establish themselves as permanent members of the maternal social network. Adolescent males on the other hand move off to join the peripheral males who live on the edge of the main troop. For the bold and curious young males the fence is an inconvenience and a challenge. By trial and error, (i.e. by taking a few electric shocks) and by watching others try, these animals were able to learn how to climb the fence without touching hot wires. Within 18 months of being moved to the site the peripheral males, intelligent and motivated, were regularly coming in and out of the enclosure. Since male dispersal is the evolved species-specific pattern of behaviour, eventually these males develop the characteristic wanderlust and go off in search of social and breeding opportunities elsewhere. There are, however, no other Japanese macaque troops in south Texas.

---

3   Other primate facility researchers and managers have tried to help us design a monkey proof fence and it is clear that when it comes to fencing, all monkeys are not equal. Snow monkeys are notoriously difficult to confine.

At first, attempts were made to contain them, as the monkeys were never intended to roam freely over the ranch. A large cage was built and they were trapped and held for a time, but eventually they escaped from this enclosure as well and we came to accept that the range of the peripheral males would include areas outside of the compound. This meant that the on-site researchers were now living within the normal range of some of the monkeys.

LIVING WITH MONKEYS 🏵

In the fall of 1982 I was living at the site in one of the researchers' trailers, collecting data for my Master's thesis. As a child I had dreamed of having a monkey for a pet. I no longer have any illusions about the joys of living with monkeys. Monkeys are smart, fast, curious, manipulative, fearless, and determined. There is an old saying that good fences make good neighbours and I believe it. The free ranging peripheral male snow monkeys did not make good neighbours.

After the peripheral males had mastered the fence, unpacking groceries from the bed of the pickup truck became a truly challenging undertaking. Usually the cab of the truck was filled with field equipment and supplies. The first time I naively tried walking away from the truck with an armload of groceries, monkeys suddenly appeared, jumped on the truck, and proceeded to tear apart the remaining bags. Fresh fruit and vegetables were the first to go, but they also took whatever sweets were available, and ran off with any interesting containers. Once the monkeys have possession of something, there is usually no chance of getting it back. I remember standing in the midday sun in a kind of standoff, unable to leave the truck, with a crowd of juvenile male monkeys watching, waiting for me to make a move. Ice and frozen food melt quickly in that heat and eventually I had to try to get the groceries inside. After one or two of these ordeals, with much running and yelling on my part, and much pillaging on theirs, I learned never to try to unload groceries without at least one other human to help me.

There were times when I genuinely believed that these monkeys were purposely harassing me. The house trailer that I lived in had an aluminium roof and in the spring of 1983 the monkeys discovered a new activity that was particularly bothersome. In the middle of the night they would suddenly begin jumping one at a time from high up a nearby tree onto the roof of the trailer, directly over the place where I slept. This sudden loud crashing noise directly overhead would cause me to bolt upright from sound sleep. The jumper would then run the full length of the trailer and jump off. The noise was deafening and this activity would go on for hours. I tried everything from cutting the branches off the tree to shooting a pistol in the air to scare them off. Nothing worked, and finally I resigned myself to being awake for two or more hours in the middle of every night.

Peripheral male Japanese macaques normally form a kind of roving all-male band that lives on the edge of the main troop. Occasionally a female will join this group, as happened in the Arashiyama West troop in the early 1980's. An old female, Matsu58, left the enclosure and all of her family there to live outside with the peripheral males. When she was in the main troop, she stayed close to the edge of it—spatially closer to the peripheral males. She was a low-ranking female in the main troop, but had considerably higher status outside. As she got older she seemed to become more surly.

At one time I tried training a young dog named Tiger to guard the groceries while I unloaded them. Tiger was part hound, and while he was never any help with the groceries, he did learn to chase the peripheral males, something he did with zeal. He never actually caught any monkeys—the males always ran away in plenty of time. Matsu58 responded somewhat differently. After suffering the indignity of fleeing with the males from this lesser mammal on a number of occasions, she began to think twice. At first she would stand her ground and threaten and lunge at Tiger. They were about the same size, six to eight kilograms. Tiger was at first quite perplexed by this, and would stop and cock his head to the side in confusion. But then he persisted in chasing her. This was clearly an outrage to Matsu58 and finally one day *she* ran at *him*, pinned him down with her strong grasping hands, and began biting him. Tiger yelped in terror and fought to free himself from the grasp of her teeth and hands. After this incident, Tiger never chased Matsu58 again. In fact, on many occasions I saw him running a group of males off toward the trees when he would suddenly catch sight of Matsu58. He would yelp and turn and head for cover. Later, when new student researchers complained that all of the monkeys look alike, I would point out that this *dog* could tell them apart.

MONKEYS ON THE INTERSTATE[4] ❧

Most Japanese monkey males join the peripheral male subgroup at about three years of age. In Texas these males have a number of options in terms of their social lives after this point. Some remain as peripheral members of their natal troop throughout their lives. Some return to the centre of the natal troop. Some leave the natal troop—which in their original habitat in Japan would mean leaving to join the periphery or main body of another troop. When Arashiyama West males take the latter option they end up wandering around south Texas alone, or in pairs if they departed with another animal. Eventually we receive word of the sightings of monkeys on another ranch, or on Interstate 35. More than one family has had its summer car trip enhanced by the sudden appearance

---

4   Also the title of a book by Jack Hanna in which he devotes a complete chapter to escaped
      Japanese macaques.

of a wild monkey at a roadside picnic area, begging for food. Usually these animals are successfully trapped and returned to the site where they may or may not wander off again. Others disappear and are presumed dead.

Occasionally the descriptions of the monkeys can become quite exaggerated. Even a fully adult male is no more than 60 centimetres tall when walking bipedally, yet they have been described by frightened ranch hands as being the "size of a 12 year old boy". Lou Griffin spent many hours in the spring of 1991 trying to track down a particularly elusive animal who was reportedly *throwing watermelons* at field workers.

The male dispersal and female philopatry which characterise Japanese macaque society present some interesting problems for the monkeys and their human managers in south Texas. In 1989 however, a situation developed that may provide a partial solution to the problem. Twenty-three years after the 1966 fission that produced Arashiyama A, (now Arashiyama West), the first fission within the Texas colony took place.

THE FISSION OF 1989 ❧

The number of individual monkeys in this colony grew steadily from 150 in 1972 to approximately 450 in 1989. This is a very large troop by wild standards, but is not unusual for a provisioned group. Rapid population growth is a fairly predictable outcome of food enhancement, whether the enhanced food supply is the result of human management of the group or the result of natural fluctuations in the food supply. Nonmanaged feral groups will usually grow to about 50 animals before fissioning into two smaller groups. Wild groups rarely become much larger than this—possibly the foraging subgroups which form under the conditions of the natural food supply are a precursor to fission. The provisioning of the Arashiyama West group in the manner described above may have suppressed fission because the food is distributed evenly and does not favour the formation of foraging subgroups. For the first 17 years in Texas the troop grew to 450 animals yet it remained one cohesive social group.

Population growth was itself obviously not a sufficient condition to precipitate a fission at Arashiyama West. In 1988 and 1989 however both environmental and social circumstances contributed the additional necessary conditions. The environment in south Texas is normally quite dry, and hot temperatures (30–40 degrees Celcius) are the norm for six to eight months of the year. The winter and spring of 1988 were unusually dry and hot, resulting in a significant decrease in natural flora and brush cover, as well as in the drying up of one swimming hole and a significant reduction in the water level in the other.[5] No crops were planted in the enclosure in either 1988 or 1989, although

---

5   Fresh drinking water was always available from a number of artificial water spigots throughout the enclosure.

they had been in all preceding years at this site (1980–87). Thus by the spring of 1988, the area within the electrified fence contained very little in the way of shade, cover, or natural forage. The area immediately surrounding the enclosure was comparatively lush, with thick mesquite brush, cactus, and a variety of other edible flora.

The troop had increased in size gradually but consistently since its arrival in Texas. By 1988, a relatively small percentage of the troop consisted of Japanese-born individuals (10%), however the central core of the troop was still made up of high ranking Japanese born animals. In the preceding years there had been a gradual loss through death of many of the older females and males, however there were no major changes in either the male or female dominance hierarchies in the winter and spring of 1988, and the internal troop dynamics were stable.

The fission appears to have begun with a 23 year old female, Pelka65. Pelka65 had always been an unusual animal in that she was very high ranking, and yet spent most of her time on the periphery of the troop. In March of 1988, Pelka65, her adult daughter, Pelka6575, and some of their children, began spending the bulk of the daylight hours away from the main troop, outside of the fenced area, resting and foraging in the brushy area immediately north. They shared this area with the peripheral males and they were accompanied by two troop females from other families. At this time, the small group had no trouble re-entering the troop at the end of each day, no aggression was directed at them, and thus there was no evidence that they were forming a permanent subgroup. In the spring and summer the troop is normally quite dispersed, so the behaviour of these animals was not noted as being highly abnormal, except in that they were leaving the enclosure entirely, when the rest of the troop was not doing so.

This pattern continued until August of 1988, when Pelka65 died. She did not appear ill before her death, and as her body was not discovered in time for an autopsy, the cause of death is unknown. The mean age at death for a female in the third decade of life in this troop is 23 and it is therefore assumed that Pelka65 died of natural causes. Following her death, the offspring who had spent their days outside of the enclosure with her moved back into the main troop, as did the two unrelated females. In September the troop became much more cohesive, as is the norm for the mating season, including the movement of the peripheral males back to the edge of the main troop. Throughout the fall and winter of 1988, the troop behaved as a stable cohesive entity. Pelka65's eldest son, Pelka6576, who was one of the troops central males, died in October of 1988.

In the spring of 1989, when the normal springtime dispersiveness had returned to the troop, a small splinter group of forty individuals, lead by Pelka6575, formed over a period of only three weeks. I am not able to describe in detail the exact process by which this splinter group formed, as it happened quickly and was primarily evident after the fact. However, it was clear to Lou Griffin, who made the observations, that the internal make-up of the splinter group was the key to the fission, and that social fragmentation occurred before spatial separation. Almost all members of the new splinter group were spatially peripheral members of the main troop prior to any evidence of a fission. The splinter group apparently established its own "identity" before it came to be perceived as a separate entity by the main troop. Unlike the daytime group formed by Pelka65 and her offspring in the preceding year, this group received aggression from the main troop when it approached within 10 meters of any of the main troop members. Generally the young peripheral males of the main troop initiated the aggression toward the newly formed splinter group, and they were consistently supported by the rest of the main troop. This aggression did not reach the level of actual physical injury to the members of the splinter group, as all observed incidence of aggression from the main troop to this new peripheral troop were limited to chases. The new troop members did not challenge the main troop, but only fled. All observed incidence of actual physical confrontation and injury were the result of interactions *within* the new group. By July of 1989, the wounding within the new troop had subsided, and a fairly stable group structure and dominance hierarchy had been established.

Membership in the new splinter troop is consistent with the normal social organisation of Japanese monkey society. For the most part, the new group is comprised of related females with unrelated males. The adult males of the new splinter troop left a peripheral position in a troop containing their close maternal relatives to join a smaller troop of females who are not closely related to them. The social and reproductive benefits of this move to these animals of the splinter troop are obvious. In addition, the splinter troop has expanded their range to include areas normally not occupied by the main troop. In the four years since the fission the two groups have remained distinct and there have been a number of transfers of males from the main troop to the splinter troop. Thus there is now another option for dispersing males.

Three identifiable subgroups of Japanese macaques are now present at the site: the main troop, the peripheral males of the main troop, and the splinter troop. The spatial integrity of the three groups appears to be maintained at all times, allowing for the differential degrees of cohesiveness during the mating and non-mating seasons. The movements of the peripheral troop appear to be determined in large part by the movements of the main troop. For example, if the main troop is at the south end of the enclosure, the peripheral troop may venture inside the fence at the north end. If the main troop moves north, the peripheral troop will immediately leave the enclosure out the north fence, into the area by the researchers trailers. This area just north of the enclosure is normally occupied by the splinter troop of Japanese monkeys and the vervet monkey group. The members of the peripheral troop seem always aware of the location of the central troop and for the most part move off willingly. Occasionally, the peripheral males of the main troop chase the members of the peripheral troop. If the main troop is at a distance the splinter troop members may skirmish with the peripheral males of the main troop but usually the peripheral troop members simply run off. Although all three groups of animals move freely about the surrounding area, this spatial separation between them is maintained. The approximately 10 metre buffer zone between the peripheral males of the main troop and the individuals of the peripheral troop is clear to the eye.

LEARNING NEW BEHAVIOURS 🐾

Prior to the fission, the lack of other troops to which dispersing males could immigrate was only one of many challenges specific to the south Texas environment. The monkeys had to learn entirely new food sources; to learn what was good and safe to eat and what was not. Several animals suffered illness after eating poisonous berries at the first site in Texas. When the researchers discovered that poisonous berries were the cause of the sickness observed in several monkeys they immediately began removing the plants from the area. This proved to be unnecessary, however, as the monkeys stopped eating the berries on their own. Prickly pear cactus is plentiful in this part of south Texas, and while perfectly safe to eat, it is very difficult to handle. Each of the numerous pads and fruits contains countless fine barbed needles. My own experience of walking too close to the plant has taught me that these needles are very easily embedded in human flesh. Prickly pear cactus however is a favourite with the monkeys and consuming the physically hostile plant is something they mastered with ease.

Rattlesnakes are numerous at the current site and the monkeys have had to learn to co-exist with them. A number of monkeys have died from rattlesnake

Japanese monkey eating a prickly pear cactus pad.

bites in the past, but the monkeys now have special behaviour patterns which they have developed to deal with this threat. By the mid-1980s, it became clear to Lou Griffin and then to me, that the monkeys had developed a new call, one which was given only in the presence of a rattlesnake. It is not a loud call, but a light, rather subtle one. It sounds like a variant of a standard alarm call, but it is distinct. I have come to rely on this call to warn me of the presence of a rattlesnake, and have been protected by it on more than one occasion.

The call is accompanied by a host of behaviours which we call the "rattlesnake reaction". Only after being exposed to this reaction did I became aware of the faint vocalisation which accompanied it. One of my first exposures to it came while collecting focal animal data on a female who was sitting under a mesquite tree, surrounded by her family. The tree was located in the creek-bed/ravine that runs the length of the enclosure in an area of fairly dense brush. I stood in the dense grass and brush with monkeys all around me. The female on which I was focussing my observations rather abruptly abandoned her social interactions and climbed the tree, followed by all of the monkeys around her. I continued to observe her, making notes in the comments section of my data sheet that all of the monkeys in the tree were staring at the ground. Looking around to see if perhaps a high ranking male had approached, and I noticed that all of the monkeys who had been nearby on the ground were gone. I was now the only one standing in the grassy area. While puzzling over this sudden change in the behaviour of the monkeys, I saw the rattlesnake in the grass a few feet away. At that moment I became aware of the vocalisation. Lou had described to me the "snake call" and this was the first time I heard it myself. Looking around I noted again that all of the monkeys had moved up into trees or out of the brushy area and that all eyes were on the snake. The monkeys on the ground who had moved out into safer territory were standing bipedally peering into the spot where the snake had been spotted. Every time the snake moved, a chorus of alarm calls and snake calls could be heard.

Once familiar with the rattlesnake alarm call I might hear it before the full "rattlesnake reaction" occurred. On one occasion a monkey "saved" me from stepping on a rattlesnake that was lying in the grass just a few feet ahead of me. She was sitting in a nearby bush and gave the call and I stopped walking even before I was aware of what I had heard. This reaction was automatic and it then took me a few seconds to realise what I had heard, locate the caller, follow the direction of her stare, and finally see the rattlesnake myself. Lou later gave this particular monkey the nickname Lifesaver.

As I came to know more of the human population in this area of south Texas, I realised that people commonly internalise a deep seated fear of rattlesnakes, even if they have never actually seen one. In conversations having nothing to do with rattlesnakes they are mentioned in the context of fear. For example, an elderly widow, describing to me her late husband, stated proudly that "He was afraid of nothing!" Almost as an afterthought and statement of the obvious she added "except a rattlesnake of course". As a newcomer to the area I lacked this fear. Interestingly, I developed a gut-level fear reaction in response to the monkeys rattlesnake call and reaction—their fear seemed to be contagious.

For years I wondered how the monkeys had come up with this new call, and how all had managed to learn it, and to learn what it meant. It is specific to rattlesnakes and it is not given incorrectly in response to other snakes. Even the chickensnake, a nonpoisonous rattlesnake mimic does not elicit the call or the response. How did they all come to know that only the rattlesnake is poisonous and how was this information passed on from one monkey to the next? How did they all learn the appropriate response to the rattlesnake alarm call? Surely they did not all see a rattlesnake bite a monkey. Even if they did, the effects of the bite would be delayed, and would not necessarily be linked to the earlier encounter with the snake. We will never know who first used the variant alarm call, but its meaning and the widespread acceptance and understanding of its meaning can probably be explained by nonverbal communication and imitation. These monkeys are highly sensitive to fear experienced by other group members; this, coupled with the behavioural reaction to the snake would send a clear message to young animals not familiar with the rattlesnake danger. When new behaviours (e.g. sweet potato washing) were observed in the Japanese monkeys of Koshima Island in Japan, the observers were fortunate enough to witness the inception of the new behaviour, and were able to follow and document its transmission in the group. With the rattlesnake call of the Arashiyama West monkeys, we can only guess that a few key animals witnessed the results of a rattlesnake bite and that their reaction to future sightings was the beginning of this new behaviour.

**Response to an alarm call: Monkeys peer into the area
where a rattlesnake was spotted.**

A DAY IN THE LIFE ❧

In spite of the rattlesnakes, heat, cactus, and roof jumping, life at the site of the Arashiyama West colony of Japanese monkeys is always fascinating. A typical researcher's day starts early, as the hour just before sun up is a wonderful time to observe the monkeys. There is enough light to see, the air is still cool, the enclosure is quiet, the monkeys are still in their sleeping locations with their sleeping partners. This is one of the best times to see revealing social interactions. The monkeys wake near dawn but don't begin moving out of the sleeping area right away. Juveniles start running and playing long before the adults think it prudent. After an hour or so the group will slowly move out to forage. The next hour or two are spent breakfasting on the planted crops or on chow and grain left on the road from the previous day's provisions. By mid-to-late morning, as the temperature climbs, the animals head back to the core area for shade and water. Here they nap and socialise—another good time to sit and observe. Provisioned food is usually scattered at mid-day. The monkeys fill up their cheek pouches and head back to the shade to eat. Afternoon is another time for rest and social interaction. In the late afternoon and early evening the monkeys move off to forage once again on the chow line and in the planted fields. Just before dusk they return to the sleeping area around the ponds and begin to settle in for the night. Night time observations are infrequent because the monkeys react fearfully to the approach of human observers in the dark, but it is clear from the noise coming from the enclosure that some social activity continues through the night.

This daily activity pattern is not unlike what has been described for wild nonprovisioned monkey troops. The once-a-day scattering of food seems to limit the disruption to this one time period, although the amount of time spent out looking for food is undoubtedly reduced. Since we have no reason to assume that the nature of the interactions within non-foraging times is affected,[6] this group is ideal for research into social dynamics. Much of the day is spent in social activity—or at least in non-feeding activity.

In the following chapters I will describe the social life of these Japanese monkeys. Several variables structure and influence behaviour, including kinship, dominance, personality, and age and a chapter is devoted to each of these. The theme of cooperation in social life is evident throughout, and a separate chapter describes the conflict and aggression that are also part of every-day social life. A further chapter describes sexual behaviour and the mating season in the Arashiyama West Colony and a final short chapter is devoted to the problems faced by the human managers of the colony and the question of the future survival of this troop.

---

6   It is not yet known what effects the large population might have on the social dynamics within the troop.

Kinship

2

THE NAMING SYSTEM 🐾

When the Japanese scientists came to know the Arashiyama monkeys as individuals in the early 1950s, they gave them individual names. One female was given the name Betta, another Rheus, another Pelka, and so on. These

Sisters

17

females were the original matriarchs of the lineages now represented in Texas. When each of these females had offspring, these offspring were given the name of their mother, to which was added the year of birth. The original female named Betta had a daughter in 1958 which was named Betta58. Betta then had two more daughters in 1959 and 1963 named Betta59 and Betta63. The same rules applied to the naming of all offspring, so when Betta59 had daughters in 1966, 1969, and 1971, they were named Betta5966, Betta5969, and Betta5971. The system is excellent in that each animal has a unique name, each containing the exact age of the individual, as well as the exact age and identity of female ancestors back to the 1950s.

When given the names of two or more animals of the same lineage, it is easy to determine the relationship between them. Betta5966 and Betta5969 are sisters—both have Betta59 as their mother. Betta5966 and Betta6368 are cousins. By examining their names it is easy to see that their mothers were Betta59 and Betta63 who were sisters with the original Betta as their mother. The following diagram illustrates these relationships:

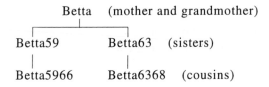

The use of this system, which gives each animal its unique name, continues at Arashiyama West to this day. Betta5966 for example has had many offspring. They are:

Betta596671	female
Betta596674	male
Betta596675	female
Betta596677	female
Betta596678	female
Betta596679	female
Betta596680	male
Betta596681	male
Betta596682	male
Betta596683	male
Betta596684	male
Betta596685	male
Betta596686	female
Betta596687	female
Betta596687	male (twins)
Betta596689	male

There is no indication in the name itself that the individual is male or female. The sex of the Betta5966's offspring is provided here for interest. Betta5966 was a very successful reproducer, giving birth almost every year. The pattern for most females is to have an infant every other year. Betta5966 died in the winter of 1990, but most of her daughters remain in the troop today. Like their mother, these females are all successful reproducers, with the oldest, Betta596671, a grandmother herself in 1989. The great-grandchild of Betta5966 has a name that is 10 numerals long: Betta5966718489. The naming system is very effective in terms of the information it contains, but some names have become unwieldy. Because this is a species in which females often have their first offspring at five years of age, there are now seventh generation individuals in some families who have names containing 14 numerals.

Each animal also has a tattoo number ranging from one to 999, and many have nicknames as well. In the 1970s when the troop was smaller and the names were still manageable researchers and managers referred to the animals by the genealogical naming system described above. Now most researchers use the nicknames or tattoo numbers as opposed to the often lengthy alpha-numeric genealogical name. Thus we avoid trying to make statements such as "I saw Betta5966718489 playing with Rheus586571768287". New researchers begin by reading the tattoo number coded on the animal's face, then consulting the census sheet to see who the animal is.

KINSHIP—MAKING SENSE OF SOCIAL LIFE ❧

The amount of information known about each animal, particularly information regarding its relatedness to others in the group, is critical to our ability to make sense of the social lives of these animals. Maternal kin relations hold macaque society together, and guide almost all aspects of social behaviour. Identifying individuals and knowing how these individuals are related to one another helps us to make sense of the monkey's social interactions. During my first visit to the colony in 1981 I felt lost and overwhelmed by the sea of identical monkey faces, and the seemingly random and chaotic buzz of interaction. We spent two or three days learning to read the facial tattoos on the animals and trying to tell the difference between a male and a female, between a juvenile and an adult. It seemed hopeless. When the director and field school instructors chatted back and forth about the monkeys ("Did you see little Deko this morning? She seems to be trying to get close to Summa." "Really? She used to be so intimidated by him. Maybe she is trying to cash in on her mother's friendship with him" etc . . .) I was filled with frustration. I was skeptical that they really could tell all those animals apart and that they were able to make sense of the apparent chaos.

On the fourth day I was assigned a small group of animals to watch. My duties were to read the facial tattoos, look up the tattoo number on my census sheet, get the family names, and thereby figure out who these animals were and how they were related. The instructor said she would be back shortly to check my observations. Up until then the interactions and movement of the animals had seemed random and chaotic. "What if they go off in different directions—who should I follow?" I asked. Calmly she looked at the group and around the nearby area and said "No, I don't think that will happen; they have just settled in here. They are very high ranking so they will not get displaced or chased off."

The group contained three adult females and a number of juveniles, the adults sitting peacefully together grooming one another and the juveniles playing in the vicinity. Consistent with the instructor's observations, the group seemed unconcerned by the activities of nearby animals. Reading facial tattoos became easy after a while, but back then it took several minutes for me to feel confident that I had even one of them correct. Eventually I determined that the tattoo numbers of the three adult females were 49, 68, and 152. I wrote them down on my clipboard and looked them up on the census sheet. They turned out to be:

> #49—Betta5966
> #68—Betta596671
> #152—Betta596677

These names revealed that I was looking at a mother and her two daughters: tattoo #49 was the mother, and #68 and #152 were her daughters. I even knew the exact ages of each of them. The instructor returned, confirming my identifications and explaining that this was the alpha female of the troop with her two daughters. I then went through the same process again with another female kin group, and after this the fog began to clear. Individual animals could be identified and the relations between them determined. The animals I identified that day have remained some of my favourites over the years.

At one time it was thought that sexual attraction between unrelated adult males and females was the bond that held primate groups together. Now we know that the most important and enduring bond in most primate groups is the mother-offspring bond, and more specifically, the mother-daughter bond. This is particularly true in Japanese macaque society, where the mother-daughter relationship persists throughout life.

Kinship is the fundamental organising principle of Japanese macaque societies. Once individuals are identified and their relationships established, much of the social interaction becomes, if not predictable, at least somewhat understandable. Knowing who is related to whom, and how, reduces the chaos and confusion to a murmur. Kinship influences almost all aspects of social life. Even the effects of age and dominance rank are much better understood within the framework of kinship. Family members spend most of their time together, eating and sleeping together, grooming one another, fighting amongst themselves, making up, and supporting each other in conflicts with nonfamily members. To illustrate the way kinship organises the daily life of a Japanese macaque, I will describe Betta5966 and her family.[7]

---

7   Although some of the behavior of this group is related to their high status in the society, the family interactions are typical of animals throughout the hierarchy.

THE BETTA5966 MATRILINE

      Betta5966 took over as alpha female in 1974 after staging a kind of coup that brought her whole low-ranking family right to the top, displacing the formerly top ranking Rheus lineage. When the troop was moved to the site near Dilley, Texas in 1980 Betta5966 was nicknamed Hatchet—presumably because she was both tough and sharp. By the late 1980s she had four adult daughters, and each has a nickname of her own. The 1977 daughter, Betta596677, was given the unflattering name Chunk by a researcher who witnessed her first estrus season in the fall of 1981. He intended it to be affectionately derogatory and the name suited her. She was somewhat pushy and had a stocky build.[8] In 1982 Chunk's younger sister, Betta596678, had her first estrus season. She was very different from Chunk. She was much more subtle and aloof in her social interactions. Her first consort partner was Rocky, the second-ranked male in the troop and the most popular male sexual partner with the females. Most first time estrus females were intimidated, if not outright frightened of him, however. He was an aggressive animal, and although aggression and dominance do not always go hand in hand, he was very high-ranking—the apparent "heir" to the alpha male spot. Unlike her age-mates, young Betta596678 did not consort with any less intimidating, less desirable males, she went straight for the top (almost). This daughter, Betta596678, was nicknamed Lady Di, shortened now to Di. Thus Hatchet's two daughters became known as Chunk and Di. Their older sister, Betta596671, had never been given a nickname, primarily because of her sedate personality. The eldest daughter of the alpha female, she behaved in accordance with her position in life. Over the next few years she came to be known as Anne. The youngest sister, Betta596679, was nicknamed Enigma because of her ambiguous and sometimes puzzling personality. This monkey family is collectively referred to by some as "the royals".[9] To summarise, the adult female members of this family in the late 1980's were:

Betta5966	Hatchet #49
Betta596671	Anne #68
Betta596677	Chunk #152
Betta596678	Di #284
Betta596679	Enigma #449

---

8   Chunk died from a disease called Valley Fever in the fall of 1992.

9   Betta596675 died of unknown causes in the late 1970's. The youngest daughters, born in 1986 and 1987, were still juveniles at the time that most of the observations were made.

Chunk (left) sitting with a female friend from another high ranking family.

The sons of Betta5966 have had various fates, but as is the norm in Japanese macaque society none have remained close to the female members of the family as adults. They have joined the peripheral males or the splinter group, some have died and disappeared over the years. The male born in 1982 is well known to me today: he is Leon, alpha male of the splinter troop.

A DAY IN THE LIFE OF A FAMILY GROUP 🌙

A typical day in the life of this family group has them, in the faint light of dawn, huddled together near the water holes at the south end of the range, awake but not yet moving. Hatchet has her yearling in her lap, and held snugly in her arms. Her two year old sits beside her, leaning into her fur. Nearby, Chunk and Di sit with fur touching and various juveniles sit near them. Enigma is at the edge of the group, and Anne is not in view. A small group of juveniles play nearby. I assume them to be members of Hatchet's family.

After a time, when the sun is higher, Enigma stands with a stretch and looks around. During the night the monkeys have become spatially very cohesive; there are many other similar family groups nearby. Enigma looks in the direction of Rocky, now the alpha male, sitting about seven meters away on the edge of a group of Wania females. The Wanias are medium-high-ranking, and Rocky is particularly friendly with two members of this family. Enigma watches for a moment, then turns to look in the direction of the juvenile play group. Another stretch and she moves off toward the roadway where she sits and begins to sift through the dirt for grain left behind from yesterday's provisions. Slowly the rest of the group do the same. Anne is now among them. Obviously she was not far away.

Occasional defensive and aggressive screams can be heard from other group members who are sorting out the inevitable conflicts of social life, but this group is so far relatively calm. Casual glances in the direction of the noise are their only reactions.

The chowline contains little in the way of leftovers from the previous day, but group members sit for a while grooming and looking around. Mostly it is mothers grooming juveniles. When Hatchet's juvenile offspring tire of her attention, they run off to join playgroups and Hatchet begins the trek out into the fields where wild and planted grasses grow. For the next few cool morning hours, the family is spread out in the field, surrounded by the rest of the troop, foraging to fill empty stomachs. While the animals forage, no subgroupings of families are discernible. The troop seems uniformly scattered, each monkey two to three meters from the next. The scene is calm, and I sit watching a dung beetle scrambling to lift its treasure up a small incline. I am tempted to help it, when suddenly a large commotion in the distance has all of the monkeys standing alert. I cannot see exactly what is going on, but adult males appear to be the primary participants in this distant conflict. Hatchet and Di both stand erect giving aggressive barks while Chunk, Enigma, and Anne watch silently. As quickly as it came, the uproar is over and all resume foraging.

By mid-morning the Betta5966 family, along with the rest of the group, move back in towards the brushy creekbed area. It is not clear who is leading whom—there is a general amble in the direction of the creekbed by all of the

A small family group heads out to forage in the early morning.

Heading out to forage.

monkeys. Once out of the field, the family groups again become spatially distinct, with different groups settling under different choice bushes and shade structures.

I focus my attentions on Hatchet, as even with a cohesive family such as this, it is not possible to keep all members within view at all times. She walks purposefully around a bush and approaches Anne, sitting in the shade. Obviously Hatchet knew she was there even though I did not. Hatchet begins to groom Anne, but after only 30 seconds or so Anne gets up and leaves. Hatchet then approaches Enigma and begins to groom her. None of the family's many juvenile members are in view at this time, but the mothers appear unconcerned. One of the many benefits of being so high-ranking is that the juvenile members of this family are unlikely to get themselves into trouble. The other monkeys generally treat them with the same deference shown to their high-ranking mothers. Enigma accepts the grooming by Hatchet and for three to four minutes Hatchet works through her fur with great concentration. A three year old runs by and Hatchet stops to look. After this she stretches out beside Enigma in an unmistakable solicitation for grooming. Enigma obliges, and they take turns grooming one another for the next 30 minutes. In this bushy area of the range visibility is reduced, and I cannot see Chunk or Di or Anne, but assume they are nearby.

This assumption is confirmed when the defensive screams of at least two immatures suddenly rouse Hatchet and Enigma, who rush in the direction of the sounds. A play group seems to have gotten carried away and a real fight has started among the participants. Two clear sides are visible as the juveniles enact the behaviour they have observed many times: each side is trying to get the other members of the play group to back them up. When Hatchet and Enigma appear they become involved as each receives clear requests for assistance from the juveniles. I am surprised to see that Hatchet and Enigma have come in on opposite sides of the fight—obviously the primary antagonists in the conflict are their offspring. Hatchet lunges at the juvenile who has been threatening her own offspring, and Enigma's defensive screams at her mother tell me that the recipient of Hatchet's threat is Enigma's offspring. Di, who has appeared on the scene, watches but does not become actively involved. The fuss quickly calms down, with Enigma and her offspring walking off together. Hatchet sits and looks around. Enigma stops under a bush and begins to groom her juvenile. Hatchet walks to a wooden shade structure on the other side of the road and begins to doze. The other juveniles have all dispersed from the area. Off under another bush, on the same side of the road as Enigma, Chunk and Di are sitting together, fur touching, eyes closed.

The sound of a truck door slamming in the distance brings forth a chorus of food calls from the troop. It is almost noon, and Lou is loading provisions onto the truck almost a kilometre away. The monkeys are familiar with these sounds and know that food is on the way. The whole troop moves purposefully down the roadway toward the gate where the truck will enter the enclosure. Hatchet approaches Enigma and stands in front of her for a moment before continuing on. Enigma follows—the earlier conflict apparently forgotten.

Chaotic activity accompanies the scattering of the chow along the road-way, but soon the animals are scattered along the roadway eating. The sound of many molars crunching many kernels of corn dominates the mid-day quiet. The family is dispersed now, with Hatchet eating alongside one of her aunts. Anne and Enigma are further down the road, separated from Hatchet by a line of 15 or so monkeys from various families. It is hot in the middle of the road, with no protection from the sun, and so while some food is eaten, much more is stored in cheek pouches. After nearly 45 minutes the roadway clears, and while less than an hour earlier hundreds of monkeys were in view, the area is now quiet and almost deserted.

I stay with Hatchet, who is gradually making her way back up the roadway toward the water holes. We pass Chunk along the way, but the rest of the family seems not to be around. After a long drink at one of the water holes, Hatchet moves toward what I know to be a prime afternoon rest spot, a shade structure tucked away in a shady low-lying area alongside the pond. When she arrives there another female kin group is resting and grooming, and one member, a young primiparous mother, is nursing her newborn. This other group is not displaced, as Hatchet has selected an unoccupied spot to settle into, but the new mother seems nervous and moves off. When Fang, one of the troop's highest ranking males approaches Hatchet for grooming, she calmly obliges, and with the proximity of both Fang and Hatchet, the other group of females moves off. Hatchet grooms Fang for a short while before joining him in a nap. They have been gradually joined in this shady haven by other adult females and their immature offspring. Di is being groomed by Chunk, and Enigma is grooming a

**Fang: High ranking central adult male with cleft
palate.**

young Wania female. Most of the animals in the vicinity are high-ranking.
Across the pond I can see Rheus6267 being groomed by her brother Rheus6271,
a medium-low-ranked natal male who has become a central group member.
Rheus6267's daughters, Butch, Bloomer, and Nubbin are napping nearby.

Eventually Fang wanders off, and Hatchet begins to contact call. This
vocalisation is not given to any monkey in particular, and at first no one
responds. After a few minutes Di approaches Hatchet and begins to groom her.
The contact calling stops. The young Wania female had been chased off by
Enigma after a transgression involving their offspring, the details of which I
missed. No one else became involved in the conflict between Enigma and the
Wania female, who now sat in the bushes a few meters away making appeasement vocalisations while looking at Enigma.

The late afternoon brings another foray out into the fields where the animals forage on the natural flora and the planted crops. When the sun nears the horizon the troop heads back to the brushy area around the water holes, for a period of social activity, of grooming and squabbling, and settling in for the night. This is another good opportunity to observe social dynamics, as family relationships, friendships, alliances, coalitions, and dominance interactions can be easily observed. When it is almost dark, I leave to walk the length of roadway to the gate and leave the animals to the unknown events of the night.

WHO ARE KIN? ✥

It should be clear from this description that much of the social behaviour of female Japanese monkeys is directly related to family. Who are the important family members? When we talk about kinship in the context of nonhuman primate studies, we mean something very different from what is meant by social and cultural anthropologists and other investigators of human behaviour. With nonhuman primates, specifically with the Japanese monkeys being described here, we use the term kinship to refer to blood relatives. More specifically we are talking about maternal relatives. During the birth season in Texas, an early morning census is conducted every day in order to find out which females have given birth. Relationships which derive from the mother-offspring bond, including sisters, cousins, aunts, grandmothers and so on, are known.

We do not know the paternal relatedness of the animals, and the animals give no indication that they do either. No consistent special relationships have been observed that suggest that fathers know their own offspring, or that any individual animal knows its father. Ultimately we hope that genetic testing for paternity will permit us to answer this question with certainty. The animals that we call sisters (e.g. Chunk and Di) might more accurately be called half-sisters. We have no evidence that they have the same father.

Kinship ties determine large parts of an animal's social network, and many aspects of the behaviour of any one animal are best understood in the context of the maternal kin network. But not all animals belong to large cohesive families such as the one described above. For one reason or another, females may find themselves without family members to provide the social network and social support that characterise the lives of others.

LIFE WITHOUT FEMALE KIN ✥

One of the first monkeys identified by the Japanese researchers at Arashiyama in the 1950's was a female born in 1954 who was given the name Ran. When I met Ran, a.k.a. Ranny, in 1981 she was already quite old. At 27 years of age she was approaching the known maximum lifespan for a Japanese

A female grooms her juvenile offspring.

Rotte 637380 (Elmer) and her infant.

macaque, and was older than most Japanese monkeys ever live. The average age at death for females who survive into their twenties is 23. Ranny was unusual not only in terms of her age, but also because she had no daughters. She had two offspring who survived into adulthood but both were male. Since male Japanese macaques tend to disperse from their natal group at puberty, sons provide little in the way of "social security" for the golden years of a female. In fact Ranny's two sons did not disperse but remained part of the troop into adulthood. The presence of adult sons however did not give her the kind of social network that daughters would have given her. Both of her sons behaved as males do, spending far less time in social interaction than do females. Males do not generally spend their days in the company of female kin. Thus Ranny lived somewhat as a loner—she had no real kin group to which she belonged. I first thought of Ranny as a lonely old monkey and I assumed she represented the standard situation for old animals. The explanation for Ranny's social isolation, however, had to do with her failure to produce any daughters which survived to adulthood, and little to do with her age.

    In the absence of a female kinship network, Ranny had no consistent social partners. She also had no one to provide her with support in conflict situations. Since kinship and dominance are strongly interrelated in this species (see next chapter), it is not surprising that Ranny was very low-ranking. Probably in an

An inseparable pair: Fatty Patty grooms her mother, Fatsu Matsu.

Betta586469, "Rue", sister of Rocky, with infant riding ventrally.

effort to avoid the risk of conflict with other animals, she tended to be very peripheral to the troop. Locating Ranny was often difficult because there were no consistent social cues as to her whereabouts. Betta5966 could always be located in the heart of the troop and in the vicinity of her large family and other high ranking families. Ranny could be anywhere out on the periphery, which at this site often meant somewhere out in the large fields. Her day to day life was very different from that of a female who had adult daughters in the troop. Her life was not organised within a tight kinship network. All Japanese monkeys are strongly motivated to be social, and Ranny certainly needed social contact. I spent many hours following Ranny and it became clear that she engaged in short affiliative interactions, primarily short grooming bouts, with a large number of other animals. Her strategy for obtaining social contact was to approach young and low-ranking animals who were also spatially distant from the main body of the troop, even if for them it was only a temporary foray out to the field. She could be characterised as having a social network made up of many weak bonds, in comparison with Betta5966 who had fewer total social interactants, but whose bonds were much stronger.

Another old female whom I saw in a similar situation had had daughters at one time. Her name was Bertha, and when I first met her she was a normal older female, with daughters and grand-daughters. Although a low ranking female, she led a life that was much more similar to Hatchet's than it was to Ranny's. She had a consistent kin network around her, and her day to day activities and social interactions took place within this framework. She could always be located in proximity to her family members. In an unfortunate series of unrelated incidences, over a 2 year period, most of the adult members of this female kin group died. In a very short period of time Bertha went from being the centrepiece of a close family group to an animal much like Ranny, without a social network at all. Since Ranny never did have such a network, she had established a lifestyle which involved being spatially peripheral and interacting loosely with many others. Bertha however was unskilled at living without a kin network and for a time was socially isolated and displaced. The kinship network that had organised her life was suddenly gone. Eventually she established a relationship with a distant family member who became her primary social interactant.

It is not only old females who find themselves in such a position. One of the smallest lineages represented in Texas is the Shiro lineage. In 1981 when I first met Shiro64 she was the only adult female member of the lineage. I came to know her because she had a special relationship with Summa, the alpha male, and she could always be found near him. They were regular grooming partners and she could count on his support in a dispute. While she had no female kin network, she was not isolated, peripheral, or low ranking. Her only female offspring was still a juvenile.

When I returned in 1985 to begin collecting data on old females, she became one of my subjects. By this time she was over 20 years of age. Summa was dead, and her daughter was an adult with an infant of her own. Shiro64 and her daughter, Shiro6479, had a very close relationship. They were a matriline of two and were almost inseparable. Shiro64 was old but was by no means lonely or isolated. While they did not have a large support base in the agonistic encounters, and they did not have a large number of potential interactants in the family, these two females enjoyed a very strong bond with each other. Neither spent much time alone.

In the summer of 1986, at the age of 22, Shiro64 died of natural causes, and it became clear that social isolation is related to kinship, not age, and can happen at any stage of the lifecourse. Shiro6479, at seven years of age, became much like old Ranny, spending most of her time alone. Because she was young and a successful reproducer she eventually produced a new social network made up of her daughters.

It is important to note that in a female-bonded group, characterised by male dispersal, kinship does not have the same effects on the lives of males as it does on the lives of females. Even for those natal males who do not disperse from the group, or who disperse to the peripheral male group but then return to the centre, their daily lives are not organised within their female kin group. Males are generally much less social than females, and spend much more of their time alone. The central males are usually associated with certain females, and these are unlikely to be members of their family. Summa, for example, was often found associating with Shiro64. Rocky now spends much of his time outside of the mating season in proximity to Wania6575 (nicknamed Adrienne). Fatboy (Rheus6271) occasionally engaged in grooming bouts with his sister, Rheus6267, but he was the exception to the rule. Most of his time was spent with a Matsu586369 (Cross-eyed Matsu). The effects of kinship on male behaviour are thus less extensive, and because of the very different life history patterns of males and females, males are much more difficult to study throughout their lives. At the Arashiyama West site there have been cases of brothers attempting to emigrate together.

CONCLUDING COMMENTS ☙

In a female-bonded Old World monkey group such as this, the enduring social group is organised around groups of related females with unrelated immigrant males, and kinship is the single most important variable influencing the behaviour and social dynamics of the group. Once individuals are identified and the maternal kin relationships known, many of the behaviours become patterned and understandable. The significance of maternal kinship as the fundamental organising principle of macaque society could only be appreciated once large numbers of animals were individually identified and then studied for many years. This became possible when Japanese scientists of the 1950's began to provide wild troops with extra food. The time that the animals spent in the feeding grounds was the time needed to learn to tell the animals apart. A new baby could be followed for years, and the basic female kin structure of the society became known. It is to be expected that a food-enhanced environment will alter some behaviours, such as the amount of time spent searching for food, but this seems a small price to pay, as provisioning made possible the kind of longitudinal research on known individuals that revealed the pattern of male dispersal and female philopatry. Longitudinal research on known individuals also revealed the importance of kinship as an organising principle of primate social life.

While male dispersal and female philopatry do characterise many primate species, several are far less female kinship oriented, and quite different social dynamics prevail. None of the apes live in female-bonded societies such as those of macaques. Mountain gorilla society, for example, is characterised by the dispersal of both sexes from the natal group. The main ties holding groups together are the individual ties between each adult female and the silverback male. There are few if any interactions among the females in the group. Interestingly, bonobo society appears to be based on female dispersal and male philopatry, and yet is characterised by strong affiliative bonds among the apparently unrelated adult females of the group.

3

Dominance

After a very short period of observation, it becomes clear that all monkeys are not equal. Some monkeys are bold and confident, moving about freely, and easily displacing others from desired resources such as food, water, and shade. Others are much more watchful and cautious, appearing nervous and hesitant in the presence of these confident individuals, and consistently giving way to them. This difference between animals' social power and privilege is usually referred to as social dominance, and the variation that exists in the group as the dominance hierarchy. The animals that have the priority of access to desired resources are described as being dominant. Those that are displaced from desired resources are said to be subordinate. Most of the terminology reflects the powerful end of the continuum, hence the term "dominance hierarchy". With a focus on the behaviour and social interactions of the less powerful individuals, we might just as well describe it as a "subordinance hierarchy".

Knowledge of the relative dominance rankings of individuals and families often allows human observers to make accurate predictions about an interaction before it happens. Lou Griffin is able to impress visitors, new researchers, and media personnel at the site by making accurate statements about what is about to happen based on her knowledge of dominance relations among nearby individuals. For example, she can easily set up a predictable sequence by standing with a bucket of peanuts and scattering them directly in front of her. As animals approach she is able to say who they are and what is going to happen. When she first scatters the peanuts, many juveniles rush in to grab handfuls and mouthfuls. At the approach of Joe, a medium ranking adult male, she predicts that the juveniles will clear out and they do. As Joe sits eating the peanuts on the ground in front of Lou, the group of juveniles form a semi-circle around him approximately three meters away. Lou says that they are waiting for him to leave before they will approach again. No, wait, here comes Di, followed by her sisters Enigma and Anne. Joe will move off when they approach. They walk directly and confidently to the peanuts and indeed, Joe willingly moves off. The juveniles move out of his way as he passes. Di and Enigma are able to obtain some peanuts, but not many, as right behind them comes their mother, Hatchet. All animals move out of her way as she approaches and takes centre stage. She sits calmly filling her cheek pouches, her daughters now sitting watching from a distance of about two meters. The juveniles have moved further out, but are still watching and waiting. Lou points out to the observers that unless Rocky

33

Several juveniles wait for access to peanuts in the foreground. They will not approach until Rocky (front, right) leaves.

appears, Hatchet will be undisturbed and can eat her fill of peanuts. But, as if on cue, Rocky does appear and when Hatchet notices him approaching she begins to quickly grab handfuls of peanuts, and at the very last moment, when he is only a meter or so away, she jumps out of the way. This causes a kind of chain reaction with everyone else shifting back a meter or so to get out of the way of those higher ranking. No one challenges Rocky's priority of access to the peanuts. Most of the adults in the area wander off, knowing that as long as he is there they will not have any chance to get close. Only the juveniles stay nearby, watching. Lou says that they are waiting for Rocky to leave before they will approach again, and several minutes later the monkeys behave exactly as she said they would. This "show" always impresses newcomers because to them the monkeys all look alike and, up to this point, the behavioural interactions appeared to follow no pattern.

FEMALE DOMINANCE AND KINSHIP

In Japanese monkey society, both males and females form dominance hierarchies. Female dominance is directly related to kinship. Whole lineages rank above and below one another. The general rule for female-bonded Old World monkeys is that females rank just below their mothers, and sisters rank in reverse order of their ages. In other words, a mother will always rank higher than her daughters, and among the daughters, the youngest will rank the highest, and the oldest will rank the lowest. This pattern exists because of the way in which female dominance is acquired and maintained.

The dominance hierarchy can be seen as the stabilised outcome of competition for resources. For females, kinship bonds play a large part in determining the outcome of conflict situations. Members of a given family or matriline typically support one another in conflicts with nonkin, and female dominance is both acquired and maintained by the quality and quantity of support that is available to an individual. Thus, females born into high ranking families tend to remain high ranking throughout their lives, relying on longstanding kin based alliance networks to provide support in situations of conflict. Members of a given family group share adjacent dominance rankings, and whole matrilines rank above and below other matrilines. The basis of the relationship between female dominance and kinship lies in the fact that dominance is determined largely by alliances, and alliances in Japanese macaque females are based largely on kinship.

Female Japanese monkeys essentially inherit their social rank. But it is inherited socially, not biologically. Since dominance refers to one aspect of the relationship between and among animals, it is not something which and individual can directly inherit, or possess, apart from the social context. To understand how female Japanese macaques inherit or acquire their kinship based dominance ranking, consider the example of Hatchet and her infants.

From 1974 until her death in 1990, Betta5966, tattoo #49, was the alpha female of the Arashiyama West troop. She deferred only to one animal—the alpha male. Sometime around 1980 she was given the nickname Hatchet. What did her high status mean to her? Her nickname is suggestive, as she was very tough and very sharp, but she was not large and was not particularly aggressive. With her many offspring, Hatchet was a nurturant and attentive mother.

Betta 5966 had priority of access to all desired resources, including food, water, shade, and social partners. Any animals that she approached were happy to have the opportunity to socialise with her, but this opportunity was mostly limited to her daughters, a few other high ranking females, and the top ranked males. Other animals stayed out of her way, and kept their infants and juvenile offspring out of her way, not wanting to risk a violation of appropriate behaviour. Lower ranking animals often fear grimaced to show their acceptance of her position and theirs.

Although the norm for these females is to have a baby every other year, Hatchet had a baby every year, which almost always survived. She was a kind and caring mother, always ready to defend her children from any dangers. In reality, this was seldom required. Hatchet's position and that of her children however, were so secure that she rarely needed to show aggression. If she did perceive any infringement on the part of another monkey towards her or her family, a single facial threat was often enough to send the offender fleeing and flashing appeasement gestures. Likely it was the fear that if Betta 5966 was not quickly appeased, the transgressor would soon be facing all of the Bettas and their canines.

This security allowed Hatchet to be a very permissive mother. She did not need to worry that her infant would get itself in trouble by committing a social *faux pas*. For lower ranking mothers this is a very real concern, and they are comparatively restrictive of their infants movements. When one of Hatchet's infants went for a toddle, it was all of the others who were wary. On more than one occasion I watched her infants approach adult central males. The males would find themselves in an awkward position: they did not want to take a chance on interacting with the infant, lest there be any misinterpretation, and yet they did not want to upset the infant by shooing it away or by abruptly leaving it. It was quite humorous to watch a tiny dark infant trying to touch a large adult male, with the male looking horrified and trying to ease himself away, as though the infant were a poisonous spider. The infant of a lower ranking female would often receive a very different reception, possibly even being slapped or threatened away, thus drawing the mother and her kin into quite a conflict.

Infants are treated by others as an extension of the mother, up to a certain point. In addition, because Japanese monkey babies, like most primates, cling to the mother's fur, the infant passively participates in many interactions before it is treated as an individual itself. Very early in life each individual learns whom it will submit to, and whom it is dominant over. It may be partly a matter of internalising a social role or social position with respect to the other members of the group. From the very beginning, an infant of Hatchet's experiences a

Betta596678, nickname: Lady Di.

"privileged" life. Like the proverbial human child born with a silver spoon in its mouth, an infant of Hatchet's knows no other pattern of interaction. The only higher ranking individual this infant ever encounters is Hatchet herself . . . until a younger sibling appears.

For the most part, all primate adults are protective of the infants in the group, but none more so than the infant's mother. Japanese macaque neonates are almost black in colour and by their first birthday they have the coat colour of an adult. These dark-coloured newborns are accorded the greatest protection. Imagine young Di as a black infant. From the beginning she learns that all others will treat her a certain way. Even when her coat colour changes and she is spending more and more time in interactions with others while not clinging to her mother's body, she can still rely on her mother's support should anyone challenge her "right of way". She knows it, and everyone else knows it. Second from the top is the only spot she knows. Then she reaches one year of age. It is birth season again and tiny black infants start to appear on the abdomens of females in the group. One day a new black infant appears on Hatchet. Enigma has been born. Although Di has been discouraged from nursing for some time now, suddenly it becomes impossible. Enigma now has the exclusive rights to this position, a position that was previously Di's and Di's alone. The real shock comes, however, when Di has her first direct conflict with Enigma, and discovers that she does not have her mother's support. Hatchet defends the infant from the rambunctious yearling and this is the beginning of a dominance relationship between Di and Enigma that may last a lifetime. Hatchet will continue to support the youngest throughout that individual's juvenile life, and by adulthood, the relationship is set. It is, for the most part, accepted by all parties.

MALE DOMINANCE ❧

In many primate species, and particularly in Old World monkeys, males disperse from the natal group. These males do not live out their lives in the same social milieu, and new relationships are continually being established. Without the kinship networks that frame the lives of female Japanese monkeys, dominance becomes a rather different thing for males. As the dispersing sex, males must repeatedly establish new relationships, and they do not have the automatic bonds of kinship to structure their social networks. For female monkeys, dominance is mediated by kinship, but for males it is usually not, at least not in the same way that it is for females.

Males form dominance hierarchies which are separate from but related to the female hierarchy. Whereas kinship explains the dominance position of most females, for male dominance kinship plays only a minor role. The question of how males acquire and maintain dominance is not nearly as straightforward as it is for females. For one thing, males interact with one another much less than do females. Many male-male dyads would rarely or never be seen interacting, and thus establishing the dominance relations among males can be difficult. The relative rankings of the males is obvious for the first four or five in the hierarchy, but becomes more difficult to determine after that.

There are several ways to become high or low ranking as a male, and these involve the opportunities that present themselves and the choices made by individual males. Individual personality factors can play a major role in both male and female dominance but even more so for males where the structural component of kinship is absent. Male dominance relations are based on alliances and coalitions (short term cooperative efforts), but these are often not normally based on bonds of kinship.

There is a popular misconception that the most dominant males have earned this position through sheer physical force—that the biggest, strongest, and/or most aggressive males will be the most dominant. In fact the building of social bonds without the kinship base to start with requires considerable intelligence and social finesse. Social skill does not necessarily correspond to these characteristics of size and strength. In fact, excessive aggressiveness could run directly counter to the need to build strong social bonds, unless it were very carefully managed and strategically expressed. Male social success—which translates into a system of support which translates into high rank—does have a tendency to improve with age and experience. Since older males tend to be the biggest males (full skeletal maturity is reached fairly late for males), the biggest males might be the most dominant. But not necessarily. Depending on the age structure of the male population at any one time there may be several fully grown males and they do not all achieve high rank.

It is difficult to provide a clear picture of the relationship between the male dominance hierarchy and that of the females. The male dominancy hierarchy is primarily about male-male interactions—each male has a dominance position with respect to other males. To this end they form both short term coalitions and long term alliances with other males to acquire and maintain dominance. However they also require the support of female kin groups, particularly for the positions at the top of the hierarchy. Establishing relationships with females is critical to the success of the most ambitious males.

Although being able to rely on specific others for support and cooperation in situations of conflict is normally an outgrowth of having developed strong affiliative relationships with these others, the situation can be more complicated than that. The alpha male and the alpha female, for example, are not always friends. From 1978 until 1983, Hatchet and Summa were the alpha female and male of the troop. Summa took over the spot of alpha upon the death of the previous male, Dai. The story of Summa's rise to this top position is not a good example of a very clever, manipulative, and ambitious male finally achieving success. Researchers who were present at the time say that Summa, a medium ranked and somewhat peripheral male, had shown no previous indication that he was conspiring to get to the top. When Dai disappeared Summa walked to the centre of the troop. Here he might have been surprised to find the second ranked male deferring to him, and to find that one female in particular was a supporter of his. Hatchet curiously stayed out of the picture, not directly supporting Summa, but also not giving her support to any other male. In a short time, Summa was walking around the centre of the troop with his tail raised high, a sure indication that a male perceives himself to be high ranking in that context. The other troop members began treating him as the alpha male. For the next five years Summa reigned with Hatchet. He did his job well, intervening in fights and protecting infants. But Summa and Hatchet were not friends in the sense that they sat together and groomed one another on a regular basis. Grooming bouts between these two were in fact very rare. Hatchet gave him her tacit support primarily by not destabilising him by supporting any other male.

Rocky was a very different case. He was born into a branch of the large Betta lineage and made use of the high rank of his matrilineage to become a high ranking central male. But, in order to make it to the position of second from the top, where he was before Summa's death, he also needed to secure the favour of the alpha female. To this end he began to show an uncharacteristic interest in infants—specifically in the infants of Betta5966. This improved his social position in two ways. First, he may have won some appreciation with Hatchet by his alloparenting behaviour. Second, he was able to win all agonistic disputes when Hatchet's offspring were in his care because he received her full support. An agonistic encounter in which he received the support of his own close female kin in addition to the support of the alpha female would almost certainly result in a victory and a subsequent rank reversal between Rocky and

Confident of his rank, even among humans, Rocky holds his tail high and asserts his dominance.

the other male. This story is suggestive of cleverness on Rocky's part, and an ability to manipulate the social context.

When Summa died Rocky took over as alpha, but it was not a direct and easy accession to the throne. He was challenged by other males and there were several days of fighting and wounding, not all of which was observed, and finally Rocky emerged as alpha male with Hatchet's support. Rocky and Hatchet had many more affiliative interactions during their reign than did Summa and Hatchet. Every mating season they were observed in a consort pairing for at least a week.

Although the hierarchies are based on somewhat different kinds of alliance systems, and each is primarily about the dominance relations between and among the members of one sex, there are obviously dominance relations between males and females. Summa ranked above all males and above all females. Hatchet ranked above all females and above all males except Summa. It is almost like two parallel hierarchies, with the female hierarchy shifted down just one notch. The undisputed higher dominance of the alpha male over the alpha female—which she does not challenge—is curious because the alpha male requires her support in order to acquire and maintain his position. However, everybody potentially suffers in times of social instability, and the alpha female is able to keep the situation stable by not challenging and destabilising the alpha male. It is in the best interests of the females to prevent instability in the male dominance hierarchy because it tends to be associated with high levels of aggression and wounding of all animals. The only time the alpha female might find herself in a conflict with the alpha male would be if one of her offspring were being seriously threatened and/or attacked by him, a situation which does not happen often. In such a case the female would be acting defensively rather than offensively. Females will support their kin in conflicts even if those conflicts are with higher ranking males.

The examples of how Summa and Rocky acquired and maintained their dominance rank illustrate that there is no single way to be or to become very high ranking as a male. The story of the alpha male who succeeded Rocky is another situation altogether. Ran68 has always been a very low ranking but central male. All his life he has kept a low profile and stayed out of trouble, never challenging males above him, always accepting his position in life. The fact that he is now alpha male continues to surprise me. Some of us refer to Ran68 as King Ralph, after a movie about a low class Las Vegas lounge singer who, due to the most bizarre and unlikely freak accident, finds himself in the position of King of England. Ran68, like his mother old Ranny, has lived a long life. Because age and tenure in a group do often correspond to increasing dominance rank in males, Ran68 found himself to be among the top five males in 1993. In a period of only five or 6 months, all of the high ranking central males, including Rocky, disappeared. Some were found partly eaten by predators or scavengers, Rocky himself apparently killed by a large cat. Since predation has not been a problem at Arashiyama West since the early to mid-1970's, this is a strange new situation. Ran68 found himself at the top of the troop simply because there were no males above him. He was not challenged for this position by any younger central males or by any peripheral males. The situation was so unexpected that no other males were poised and ready to move in, although a number of young "movers and shakers" are now lining up just below him. Perhaps the females support and defer to him because he represents stability and endurance in a time of danger and rapid change. For me, Ran68 as alpha male is a very strange sight. He himself does not look comfortable in the position—when he approaches a high priority food item he does so somewhat cautiously, as though he himself does not expect others to move out of his way. But they do. At 25 years old, Ran68 is much older than most males ever live to be. The next oldest male in the troop was born in 1977—a full 9 years younger than Ran68. Although he is strong and healthy, Ran68 cannot be expected to live for much longer, and the humans at least are thinking about who will replace him.

The second ranked male in the troop now, just below Ran68, is an 8 year old male who has yet to reach skeletal maturity. His nickname is Randy, and his genealogical name is Betta596685. Randy is a son of Hatchet and a younger brother of Di, Enigma, and Anne. Here is a case of a high ranking natal male, a male born into the group, staying in the group and achieving high rank. Randy combines an aggressive, pushy personality with an alliance system which includes strong kinship ties. If and when he succeeds Ran68 as alpha male, an unusual situation will prevail: the alpha male and female will be brother and sister. Recall from Chapter One that the alpha male of the splinter troop which formed in 1989 is Leon, Betta596682. As the pattern of male dispersal breaks down we are beginning to see maternal kinship as a major factor in male dominance relationships.

THE SOCIAL CONTEXT OF DOMINANCE

It should be clear by now that for both males and females, dominance is something that occurs within the social context. Getting the support of others is a fundamental characteristic of any agonistic encounter. Being able to form alliances and coalitions is crucial to the ability of an animal to rank above another and to "win" in a conflict situation. How many others an individual can get to back it up in a fight, and how high-ranking these others are, determines success or failure in a conflict.

There is only one alpha female, and only one alpha male and all other animals are dominant to some and subordinate to others. While for females the rule of ranking just below your mother but over all of your older sisters generally holds, the actual outcome of each dominance interaction will be affected by a host of contextual variables. First and foremost, is your family nearby? How much higher or lower ranking is your opponent? Is her family nearby? What adult males are present? What is the nature of the conflict? How motivated are the players to win the dispute? All of these things will affect the outcome of a dominance interaction and thus dominance, a complex form of social power, cannot be measured by any one interaction. Even very low ranking animals will win some disputes with higher ranking others. So contextual phenomena is not easy to reduce and measure. In fact, a typical fight in a Japanese macaques society may involve many animals and many vocalisations, but little actual contact. Often it is not clear which side "won".

The social context has sometimes been seen as a kind of "noise", complicating and obscuring one's view of the dominance hierarchy. Some researchers have attempted to remove this "noise", the complicating variables of social context, and thereby see the "real" dominance relationship between two animals. If animal A is dominant to animal B sometimes, and it seems to depend on who is around, researchers might try removing animals A and B from the social context, and throwing a peanut between them to see who is "really" dominant. The problem with this method is that if one of the animals were consistently able to get the peanut, then this test would only tell us which of animals A and B are able to get the peanut when they are removed from the social context. But dominance does not operate in, and did not evolve in such a setting. The relationship between A and B is part of social context, and we cannot understand dominance by distorting its very nature.

Dominance refers to an aspect of the relationship between individuals and is not a characteristic of an individual which exists apart from the social context. If any member of Hatchet's family were to be relocated to another social group, that individual would lose the context which gave it its rank. Chunk is a very high ranking female. However, if Chunk were trapped and sold to a zoo colony which contained a group of females related to one another, she would most definitely find herself to be a very low ranking animal. Even within the context of her own colony in Texas, if she strayed too far from her family and got into a skirmish with another female whose family was nearby, she would almost certainly lose.

MALE-FEMALE FRIENDSHIPS AND ALLIANCES ❧

As was discussed above, males need the support of females to obtain high dominance rank. For females, it is the female kin, and female friends, who most often provide agonistic support. However there are situations in which females rely on the support of specific males to improve their social position. Some females form friendships with specific adult males and may be able to win dominance interactions because of support received by them. Cross-eyed Matsu was a fairly low ranking member of the large but low ranking Matsu family. Apart from her own daughters and a handful of others, few monkeys deferred to her. But she did have a special relationship with an adult central male, Rheus 6271 (Fatboy), and she did try to use this friendship to win disputes. On one occasion I observed her threatening a much higher ranking Meme female, trying to displace her from a pile of peanuts. Rheus 6271 was sitting nearby but none of the Meme females were in sight. All of this no doubt factored into Cross-eyed Matsu's decision to attempt to displace Meme. Meme responded by immediately

Adult female grooming adult male.

looking around and assessing the social context. Had her family been available she might have reacted strongly to the outrage of being threatened by Cross-eyed Matsu. But under the circumstances, realising she had no reliable support available, and that Cross-eyed Matsu might have, she merely returned the threat, watching carefully to see the reaction of Rheus 6271. Although he was known to support Matsu, in this instance he did not become involved. Both females were watching to see what he would do; both would decide what to do next based on his response. Without the involvement of any additional parties the interaction did not escalate. Cross-eyed Matsu gave up the attempt to displace the higher ranking Meme from the peanuts, and Meme continued to eat. Moments later Meme was easily displaced by the approach of two females from the higher ranking Deko family.

Forming friendships with central adult males is a strategy sometimes used by females without a wide base of kin support. Most of the central males tend to have at least one female who has formed a friendship with him. The friendship involves the female maintaining proximity to him, engaging in social grooming with him, and supporting him in conflict situations. She may also receive his support. Summa had a very close relationship with Shiro64 who was the matriarch of a tiny low ranking family. Pelka70, an adult central male, was always found with Sissy in proximity. Sissy was a female who was orphaned when she was still a juvenile and who had no other close female kin relationships. For several years prior to his death in 1993, Rocky had a strong friendship with Adrienne (Wania6576). When he died suddenly in an unsuccessful confrontation with a predator, Adrienne disappeared. For more than a week she was gone and presumed dead. When she returned she did so carefully, maintaining a low profile and avoiding direct contact with high ranking females. Two months later, Adrienne could most often be found in the vicinity of the new alpha male, obviously trying to establish a friendship with him. She continues now to have four adult sisters in the group, but has chosen not to rely on them for her social network. Without Adrienne, these Wania sisters are relatively low ranking.

SUBORDINANCE AND THE DIFFERENCE BETWEEN HIGH AND LOW RANK ❧

What is it like to be low ranking, to be born to a low ranking mother? Is this individual destined to be a loser for life? If high rank gives an animal confidence, security, freedom of movement, priority of access to desired resources, and guaranteed support in situations of conflict, does a low ranking animal lack all of these?

From the above description, most would agree that it is better to be high ranking than low ranking. However in many ways the lives of low ranking animals are very similar to those of high ranking ones. Within their own families at least, these animals experience similar patterns of affiliation, conflict and conflict resolution. They spend their time with their kin group, grooming, sitting, and feeding. They fight among themselves and they back each other up in fights with outsiders. The majority of their interactions involve kin who are of similar rank. They have the same kind of predictability in their interactions with one another as do high ranking animals. Cross-eyed Matsu may be low ranking in the group as a whole, but most of her interactions are with other Matsu's. She ranks just above her daughter, Woolley, and just below her two sisters, Sally and Lifesaver. In this respect her day to day social interactions, at least within her primary social network, are not that different from Chunk's, who ranks above her own daughter, but below her sisters Di and Enigma.

Of course there are some differences. Low ranking animals have to be more watchful of the location of higher ranking animals. In normal daily travel, the Bettas can go almost anywhere and not find themselves facing the wrong crowd. If they walk into an area and find a group of Matsus present, they will simply displace them. The Matsus will get up and leave, and the Bettas will take the spot, if they want it. Conversely, the Matsus would not want to inadvertently find themselves in sudden proximity to Hatchet and her family. This would be a "breach of etiquette", and the Matsus would be vulnerable to an agonistic attack. At the very least, the Bettas would chase them off. Low ranking animals, then, are much more vigilant of the comings and goings of high ranking animals, because low ranking animals are the ones that would be negatively affected by finding themselves in the wrong place at the wrong time.

Sally, a member of the low ranking Matsu family.

In the Arashiyama West troop of Japanese monkeys in Texas, the highest ranking males and females also form the central core of the troop. The rest of the troop follows them. So while Hatchet is aware of the location of her own family, she need not be keeping her eye on any other specific family group at all times. Most of the rest of the central core, however, are aware of her movements and those of her kin.

Related to this is the relative freedom that higher ranking animals have with respect to infant care. High ranking animals can afford to be more permissive with their infants, because the nature of social dominance is such that these infants carry with them their mother's social rank. A low ranking female must be much more cautious and restrictive—she cannot afford to have her socially naive youngster get itself into trouble with the many higher ranking animals in the group.

Another difference between high and low ranking animals is the frequency with which they use submissive signals. The most obvious submissive signal used by these monkeys is the "fear grimace". The fear grimace is a facial expression directed by one animal toward another, and it indicates fear and a kind of pleading apology. This signal is meant to appease the receiver—to prevent any further aggression or potential aggression. The fear grimace involves the lips being drawn back from closed teeth. Low ranking animals fear grimace to high ranking animals when they find themselves in a face to face situation with one. They do not regularly fear grimace to animals adjacent in rank, that is, to their own family and friends. The alpha male may never use this signal himself, however he receives it often. Young males fear grimace to him regularly. Hatchet as well had probably forgotten how to fear grimace by the time she died. But one of the things I remember about watching her was how often a passerby would flash a fear grimace in her direction—sometimes she wasn't even looking! It was as if the lower ranking animal did it "just in case". When she was looking and did see it, she seemed to think it appropriate. She might ignore the animal, or she might flash a threat face in return, as if to say, "right, and don't forget it".

One of the fundamental functional attributes of dominance is that it confers a priority of access to choice resources. At feeding time, particularly when the animals are receiving something of high priority, like fresh fruit, the lower ranking animals must wait. They try not to get between a higher ranking animal and a desired food item. Because the food is scattered along a roadway of perhaps a quarter of a mile, every animal is able to get access to some food. But when only a very limited amount of choice food is available, the lower ranking animals are unlikely to get any. Sick animals are sometimes given medication hidden in a banana or a caramel, and if the sick animal is low ranking, the job of getting the medication to it is much more difficult. The sick individual must be located when few others are around. A very low ranking animal will not even attempt to pick up a caramel thrown right beside it if a higher ranking animal is nearby.

It is often assumed that high ranking animals fight more, and are generally more aggressive than are low ranking animals. While it is true that low ranking animals show more submissive signals, or at least face fewer in the group to whom aggressive signals might be given, it is not true that high ranking animals are any more aggressive, or likely to fight, on a day to day basis. High ranking animals may fight very little. Intra-family conflicts would be no more common in high than in low ranking families. Fights between families would also not be more common, although high ranking animals win more.

Life is not all misery and deprivation for low ranking animals. They simply do not have all of the same freedoms and privileges that high ranking animals enjoy. My observations of animals in captivity, (e.g. zoos) have led me to believe that under these circumstances the lowest animal in the group might suffer from harassment. Such harassment of low ranking animals very rare in the Arashiyama West colony.

Sitting female fear grimaces to the smaller female who is threatening her.

IMPORTANCE OF A HIERARCHY ❧

The dominance hierarchy is probably best interpreted as representing the stabilised outcome of the competition for resources. The hierarchy itself provides all animals with a system of rules, and with some predictability in their social lives. While the proximate benefits of high dominance rank seem obvious enough, it is also true that low ranking animals benefit from the existence of the hierarchy. Without it all animals would suffer from a life of unpredictability and chaos, where every interaction over a resource involves a whole new open competition. The somewhat stable differential priority of access to resources might be seen as a necessary trade-off for the gains of living in a social group. While it is no doubt better to be high ranking than low ranking, it is better to be low ranking than to live in circumstances where constant fighting is needed to settle the ongoing competition for desired resources. Periods of instability or change in either the male or female hierarchies are associated with high levels of aggression and wounding, and this is suggestive of what life without the rules would be like. In marginal environments where resources are in short supply, low ranking animals may suffer more from the reduced access to those resources, but for this colony in Texas, where food is plentiful, they benefit from the stability that the hierarchy provides, without paying a big price in terms of resource access.

DOMINANCE AND REPRODUCTIVE SUCCESS 🜚

High rank does have its rewards, and these can be seen in the daily lives of the animals. This has led many researchers to think about the functional benefits of high rank, and about all of the ecological, social, and evolutionary benefits of being high ranking. There is a widespread perception that social dominance is directly linked to reproductive success, particularly in males. Whether through male-male competition or through female choice, high ranking males are supposed to have automatic access to estrous females and therefore to sire the most offspring. If the dominance hierarchy represents the stabilised outcome of competition, then high ranking males should have already "won" this "fight" over access to females. For their part, females should be choosing high ranking males because they are successful and their offspring may benefit from this parentage.

This is a very complex and controversial area of investigation. In this Japanese macaque colony it is safe to say that there is no clear and direct relationship between high rank and high reproductive success.[10] Two very large matrilines in the Texas troop, the Matsus and the Bettas, are both very successful in terms of reproduction. One is very high ranking, the other very low ranking.

Against the traditional view that females passively accept the sexual advances of the winners of male-male competition, I must emphasise that female Japanese monkeys are nothing if not active players in the mating game. The image of passive females simply waiting for high ranking males to approach them is simply not reflective of mating season behaviour. Females actively solicit some males, and actively reject others. High rank, or some aspect of it, may be one factor in the choice of some females, but it by no means determines all choices made by all females.

Pelka65 was a fairly high ranking mature female, who was experienced at the mating game. Never did I see her courting or accepting the courtship advances of any of the high ranking males in the troop. On several occasions, however, I did find her involved in what appeared to be "clandestine" matings with low ranking and/or peripheral males, hidden from the view of the main body of the troop. The nervousness of both Pelka and the specific male partners during these consorts suggests that the status of the male was an issue of some kind, and that these interactions could be expected to bring on some kind of interruption or interference if observed. Nonetheless, Pelka was taking the chance and appeared actively choosing not to mate with the high ranking males.

During the 1982 mating season, the alpha male in the troop was Summa. While he was without a doubt the focal centre of the troop and was regularly followed around by many of the central troop females, Summa was not the

---

10 L.M. Fedigan, S. Gouzoules, H. Gouzoules, and N. Koyama. 1986. Lifetime reproductive success in female Japanese macaques. Folia Primatologica. 47:143-57.

object of widespread sexual interest. Outright competition between adult males for access to estrus females is something I have never observed in the Japanese macaques in Texas. Images of male deer ramming antlers in a mating season contest are very popular, but nothing directly comparable occurs in these monkeys. If the dominance hierarchy reflects the stabilised outcome of such competition, the highest ranking male is already the winner, and should get to go first to desired resources. Or the "desired resource" should be choosing to mate with him. Why weren't the females interested in Summa in this way? What is the point of being the highest ranked animal if it does not provide reproductive advantages? From an evolutionary point of view, being able to get all the good food is inconsequential if one does not leave descendants. Could not Summa, by virtue of his social status and power, ensure himself access to estrus females?

The answer to this second question is actually yes . . . sort of. Summa could, if he were so inclined, fairly easily ensure that no other adult males could get close to a specific female. He could use his high rank to keep other males away. Since his alpha position in the troop was unquestioned, all he had to do was to monopolise the space around a certain female, thereby preventing other males from gaining access to her, and preventing the female from gaining access to other males. I observed him doing this on more than one occasion.

Skitsy, a female born in 1977, was the target of Summa's "affections" for a period of several days during the 1982 mating season. He followed her everywhere, and was never more than a few meters away. For at least the first five days of this, she showed no interest in mating with Summa. Perhaps she was intimidated by him because of his position as alpha male. She had had no previous experience interacting with him. Or maybe she just did not want to mate with him. But ultimately she had no other options, that is, no other suitors, because no other males came near her. On the sixth day, she was observed mating with Summa, and the ensuing consort lasted for another five days.

If Summa were in pursuit of a particular female, he would have to follow her around, monopolising the space around her, and thereby keeping other males away. This strategy would not be available to lower ranking males, as they would not, by their sheer presence, be able to keep other males away. But for Summa this is a time consuming and potentially costly strategy because it does not, in and of itself, guarantee that the female will mate with him. On another occasion Summa was in pursuit of a particular female for many days, and they were never observed mating.

Female choice is a powerful force affecting who mates with whom in the Arashiyama West troop of Japanese macaques. Perhaps a better strategy, in addition to working out one's position with respect to the other males, would be for these males to try to be attractive to the females. Male-male interactions are not the final key to success at male-female interactions. If males want females, they need to deal with females, to make themselves the objects of female choice.

We do not know precisely what features render males attractive to females. We can make many predictions from theory about what kinds of males should be chosen, but it often doesn't work out that way in the field. Summa, for example, should have been very desirable. He was high ranking, and arguably had whatever "good" genes had contributed to his high rank. Females should "want" those genes for their offspring. Or we might expect females to choose males who show signs of willingness to make an investment in offspring (i.e. good fathers). Rheus 6271 was such a male, but while Cross-eyed Matsu was apparently committed to him, the rest of the females were uninterested.

Dominance does not equal reproductive success in this colony, however, there are some intriguing individual situations. Rocky, the second ranked male until Summa's death in 1983, has always been a favourite among the females. It is not an exaggeration to say that females lined up for access to Rocky. When Rocky was involved in a consort with one female, two or three other females were often following the pair around. Although these females were not fighting outright among themselves, they were nonetheless in obvious competition. In these cases, a very high ranking female might be waiting in the lineup. Rocky also did not necessarily choose the highest ranking available partner.

What made Rocky so attractive to the females? This is a question that many of us have pondered over the years. Yes, he was high ranking, but there had to be more to it than that. The males immediately above and below him in the hierarchy had nothing like his level of mating season popularity. In the mating season of 1982, when I observed Rocky's popularity for the first time, Summa was alive and Rocky was second from the top. Two conspicuous aspects of his personality were often discussed.

First, Rocky was an elaborate "courter". Males have a number of courtship behaviours which they may display, and Rocky was particularly skillful in his use of these various behaviours and gestures. He would lip quiver and prance and strut and whirl around in front of the females. Although I never witnessed it, previous researchers described to me a striking gesture in which he would approach a female, reach under her chin with his hand, and holding her chin, look deep into her eyes. Females did not flee screaming from this gesture, which we might expect under other circumstances. Monkeys do not normally look one another in the eyes—this behaviour is threatening.

The second salient aspect of Rocky's personality was that he was aggressive, particularly during mating season. Mating season is characterised by an increase in chasing and wounding behaviour on the part of the males. The chasing behaviour of males during the mating seasons ranges from those that appear to be "not serious" and which do not end in physical contact to those that are very aggressive and which may result in biting and wounding of the female who received the chase. The distinction between these two kind of chases was sometimes clear, and they could be recorded as either a courtship chase or an aggressive chase. Rocky was an ardent chaser, but the difference between a courtship chase and an aggressive chase is not absolute, and with Rocky, more than any other male, I saw chases during the mating season end in actual aggression, with the female being pinned down and pinched or bitten. The females seemed to take all chases seriously, realizing the possible aggressive conclusions to them, and with Rocky in pursuit the females fled with full force.

Not all females showed an attraction to Rocky, and we do not know whether he actually sired many, or any, offspring. The general impression that other researchers and I have always had is that females stay away from aggressive males. Thus the coincidence of aggressiveness and mating success in this one male is intriguing. Since aggression within an established consort is much less frequent, possibly the safest place to be, with respect to a male like Rocky, is *in a consort* with him. Certainly for the duration of a consort with Rocky, his partners shared the benefits of his high rank. And for the duration of a consort with Rocky, his partners were completely safe from the mating season aggressiveness of other males.

In terms of the relationship between dominance and reproductive success, and the case of Rocky who had both high dominance rank and high mating success, Rocky's high level of social skill should not be forgotten. Some primatologists have suggested that high rank and mating success are two variables which may in fact both be related to a third variable, that of social skill. Good social skills could be leading males to have both high rank and a high level of mating success, and thus the two are sometimes correlated not because one (dominance) is causing the other (mating success) but because both are caused by the third variable of social skill. The story of Rocky's rise to power is but one example of his cleverness as a social strategist and manipulator. Maybe his elaborate courtship is another example of his skillful use of social signals which are available to all males.

AN END TO THE REIGN OF BETTA5966   🐾

After making it to the position of second ranked male, Rocky resumed his previous pattern of ignoring infants. The pattern reappeared following the 1990 death of Hatchet. She was 24 years old and died from complications following a stroke. The death of Betta5966 provided us with the rare opportunity to see the replacement of the alpha female. Strictly following the rule of youngest daughter ranking highest, it would be expected that her youngest daughter, Spock (Betta596686), would take over as alpha female. However, with young adult females, the general rule still depends to a certain extent on the presence of the mother. Also, the role of the alpha female is somewhat different from any other slot in the hierarchy. Those of us familiar with the individuals involved did not expect Spock to take over. Even though she was technically an adult, she was too young—her position with respect to her sisters still depended on Hatchet's presence. Enigma was the obvious candidate, yet based on personality traits, many suspected that Di would replace her mother. It was also possible that this was the opportunity that some other female was looking for, and that there might be some major instability in the female dominance hierarchy and some major shifts of power.

In fact, nothing so eventful took place. There was no outside takeover, and for a long while none of the daughters emerged as a clear alpha female. We were accustomed to this role being filled by Hatchet, and she had had such a strong presence that it seemed as though her death left a vacuum that no one could fill. The power peak at the top of the female hierarchy was levelled with her death. For several months, interactions among the daughters were not decisive and gave no consistent indication of who was the highest ranking.

Betta5966 died early in 1990, and within a few months I had the opportunity to see Rocky engaging in his legendary infant care behaviour. He carried, groomed, followed, and protected a young female named Betta 59667889—the yearling daughter of Di. This yearling, nicknamed Carmen, was distinctive in appearance because she was very small for a yearling, the smallest of her birth cohort, and because she had very blond fur. Rocky's behaviour with respect to Carmen was much more than just tolerance. He was actively nurturant with Carmen—he acted like a mother, and to my eye, totally unlike himself.

Di is now the alpha female of the Arashiyama West troop. Those of us familiar with Hatchet's reign had to become accustomed to the very different leadership style of Di. In 1974, Hatchet took over the position with the force of her personality, with her cleverness, and with her superior social skills. The conditions of Di's becoming alpha, and the personality of Di herself, were very different. The situation made it clear how the personality of an individual filling a social role can be confused with the characteristics of the role itself. Di is the alpha female now, but she is not Hatchet.

What Rocky's involvement with Carmen had to do with Hatchet's death and replacement is not fully understood. By this time he was alpha male, so he did not appear to need it for himself. The situation is reminiscent of his own rise to power though, and it may be more than just a coincidence that this behaviour reappeared at a time of change in the female hierarchy. Perhaps his motive was the avoidance of the potential "chaos" that could result from major instability in the female hierarchy. Or perhaps his motive had more to do with his own stability and that of the male hierarchy, since these did still depend on the good relations and continued support of the Betta5966 family, and of the future alpha female.

4

Personality

One year, after sitting in on several of my primate behaviour lectures, my teaching assistant, a graduate student studying in the area of socio-cultural anthropology, approached me to clarify some of the material. She was particularly interested in the fact that the monkeys were described as individuals, that they were treated as though they had personalities, individual motivations, and the ability to be active strategists and players in a complex social arena. She was not familiar with the behaviour of nonhuman primates before sitting in on these lectures, and had assumed these things to be uniquely human.

It will be obvious from reading up to this point that each monkey is an individual, with its own distinct personality. I take this for granted now—so much so that I forget that at one time I did not know it. When I first started studying the monkeys of Arashiyama West I could not tell them apart, and was skeptical of the personality characteristics that were attributed to them by those who knew them as individuals. It is not uncommon for people unfamiliar with the true complexities of nonhuman primate social life to assert confidently that such anthropomorphic descriptions are invalid, that these attributes do not exist in the animals, and that they are projected on to them by the human observer. (Oddly enough some of these same skeptics will readily describe the personality of their cat.) That individual prosimians, monkeys, and apes have personalities of their own, and that this is an important theme in social life, is an unavoidable conclusion for all of those humans who have spent any time systematically watching primate social behaviour. I have yet to meet a person with such exposure who denies this.

After reading the previous chapters, it should be clear that individual personalities and social circumstances play a major role in determining the social dynamics of the individuals in the group. While kinship and dominance frame much of what happens in social life, the specifics of any behavioural interaction will vary depending on which individual animals are involved. Is the dominance hierarchy of females absolutely fixed and unchanging, given the fact that is so closely tied to kinship? Is an animal born into a low ranking family always low ranking? The answer to these questions is no. The family dominance that an animal inherits is like a hand of cards it is dealt. Personality plays a major role in determining how these cards are played, and whether the hand is accepted at all.

**Juvenile male member of the Deko family relaxing in the fork of a tree.
Dekos are noted for their prominant ears.**

The most striking story of personality and opportunism in the Arashiayama West troop, I came by second-hand. In 1972, when the monkeys first arrived from Japan, one of the Japanese scientists commented to one of the Western scientists to keep an eye on a young female from a medium low ranking family. He suspected that she had plans. The female was only 6 years old, just barely an adult, and the American researcher dismissed as unlikely the idea that this little female could amount to anything. Two years later this young female from the medium low ranking Betta family staged a coup that ultimately lifted her entire lineage to the very top.[11] The female was Betta5966, later to be nicknamed Hatchet. Even as a subadult she had shown signs of being a very

11 For a full description see Gouzoules, 1980. A description of genealogical rank changes in a troop of Japanese monkeys (Macaca fuscata). Primates. 21:262-67.

Betta5966. Nickname: Hatchet.

opportunistic and motivated individual. Japanese researchers, always sensitive to the individual personalities of the monkeys, had seen signs that she would not just accept her station in life, and they were absolutely correct. Of all the monkeys that I have known, Hatchet had by far the most powerful personality.

The very different leadership style of Di in the alpha female spot, compared with that of Hatchet before her, (as discussed in the previous chapter) is another good example of how the distinctive personalities and behaviour patterns of different monkeys can affect social dynamics, and in that case, how a particular social role is filled.

PERSONALITIES IN THE PELKA FAMILY ❧

A favourite monkey of mine was Pelka6078, nicknamed Imo after the famous wheat and potato washing Imo of Koshima Island. She was a precocious animal, always trying to get into the pockets of the manager and the researchers even though this kind of habituation is discouraged. Imo was born to a very low ranking mother, yet from the time she was five years old she was obviously looking for an opportunity to move up. On a regular basis Imo would cautiously make her way toward the centre of the troop, trying not to attract too much attention. She would then place herself on the edge of Betta5966's family and sit there, trying to appear nonchalant, and yet clearly monitoring every move. She missed no opportunity to direct submissive signals in the direction of Chunk or Di or Enigma, hoping to establish a grooming bout with one of them. If there was any kind of conflict involving a nonfamily member, Imo would rush in to offer her support to the Bettas, bravely challenging the transgressor. The problem was that the animals likely to skirmish with the Bettas would be quite high ranking themselves. When they spotted the lowly interloper in the midst of the battle, they would invariably focus their attacks on her, and the Bettas would then support them! Poor Imo would be chased far away, back to where she came from, to nurse her wounds and get up the nerve to try again, perhaps another day. Over the years I was struck by her persistence in the face of hopeless circumstances. She had the motivation, without a doubt, but she lacked the skills and maybe the opportunity to make things change. Sadly, Imo disappeared at age 10 without ever gaining much in the way of dominance.

Imo's mother, Pelka60, was a very low ranking female with little in the way of reliable agonistic support. Pelka60 accepted her low rank and spent her time avoiding interactions with the many higher ranking individuals in the group. Imo was her primary social partner, although Imo was obviously not satisfied with the social network she inherited at birth. Pelka60 lived out her life as a very low ranking animal. She was never in any position to assist Imo in her desire to rise in the hierarchy.

Pelka60 had a younger sister, Pelka65, who was a very different animal in several ways. These two sisters were not close as adults—Pelka60 would have been a young adult when her sister Pelka65 was born. Pelka65, essentially without a tight family group, had a strong personality and through the use of it, came to have a position of medium to high rank in the troop. Additionally, she tended to spend her time near the periphery of the main troop. Perhaps she just gave the impression of being high ranking because she seemed so independent, and gave out few submissive signals—unlike her indisputably low ranking sister. Also unlike old Ranny, who wandered around the periphery apparently in search of someone to interact with, Pelka65 seemed to like being on her own, and also to have no trouble finding a medium to high ranking grooming partner if she wanted one. She had a number of female friends from other families in addition to her own sons and daughters. Pelka65, you will recall from chapter one, was instrumental in initiating the fission of the Arashiyama West troop in 1988-89, and her daughter, Pelka6576, went on to become the alpha female of the splinter troop. It is curious that Imo, so obviously motivated to improve her position in life, did not try to affiliate with her aunt and cousin, who were able to alter their own social positions considerably over the course of their lives.

SKINK ❧

Skink is the nickname of Midori647184. The Midoris ranked below the Bettas when the troop came to Texas in 1972, but following the genealogical rank changes initiated by Hatchet in 1974, the Midoris moved up to become the second highest ranked lineage in the group. When Hatchet moved to the top she took almost the entire Betta family with her, plus a few others which included the Midoris. Researchers familiar with the troop during the 1970's described the Midoris as a "noveau riche" family because of the sudden change in their status. Since my first exposure to the Midoris they have been the second highest family, and very central in the main group. It thus came as a great surprise when, during the fission of 1989, Skink left her very high ranking and central family to join the mostly low ranking peripheral animals of the splinter troop. Pelka6576 took over immediately as alpha female of this troop, but Skink definitely had plans. She worked very hard to get near the top of the hierarchy in the splinter group. She received no help from Leon, the alpha male, but she did have a brother who also joined the splinter group (nicknamed Obe, short for Obe Wan Midori), and she did get some consistent support from him. Late in 1991 Skink began to challenge Pelka6576 directly, and by the end of that year she had taken over the alpha position. Her juvenile son, Skunk, has already distinguished himself by carefully picking fights with monkeys and humans whenever Uncle Obe is within range.

THE LOW RANKING BETTAS ❧

The Betta63 branch of the Betta family has been low ranking for all of the time that I have known these monkeys. From my experience, Betta63 had nothing in common with the other Bettas, and the family relationship was something one could easily forget. I asked Linda Fedigan, who worked with the troop in the 1970's, why Betta63 did not rise in rank with the others in 1974. She replied that "Betta63 did not rise in rank because she did not want to. Betta63 was always retiring, shy, peripheral, and quiet except for her deep booming voice (inherited by her daughter Froggy). Like Froggy, Betta63 really lived for her babies, loved them to dickens, and stayed away from her fractious sister Betta59. She showed no sign of wanting to be part of the in-crowd."

THE HIGH RANKING WANIAS ❧

As anomalous as the low ranking branch of the high ranking Betta family, is the high ranking branch of the low ranking Wania family. Again, personality is at the root of the different fortunes of the descendants of this group. Wania65

Lou Griffin allows Wild Eyes to inspect her two month old daughter.

rose in rank because she was a "political" animal like her cousin Pelka65. Using a very different strategy to change her circumstances, Wania65 formed an alliance with Summa and spent her time in proximity to the central gang of Betta5966 and company. The alliance with Summa did not in itself raise her rank, but was an indication of her interest in politics. She was often manoeuvring for position, and produced a strong contingent of offspring who looked exactly like her and defended her. Thus she also had the benefit of strong family alliances. Her daughter, Adrienne, was similarly motivated to secure her own high status and did so by becoming a constant companion of Rocky.

SCOOTER AND ROCKET ᔈ

Often persons not familiar with the monkeys, and unable to distinguish one from another based on appearance, will come to know a single animal in a very short period of time. These identifications are often based on that monkey's distinct behaviour patterns. Scooter was a juvenile male monkey who moved between the peripheral male group and the edge of the main troop. Scooter had a pattern of singling out individual humans for harassment and intimidation. This kind of unique personality and behaviour of some individuals can lead to problems involving the human caregivers and observers.

The example of Scooter is tame compared with that of Rocket, the younger brother of Rocky. Born in 1984, Rocket is now a young adult male. Over the past few years he has become more and more of a problem due to the fact that he has virtually no fear of people. The monkeys of Arashiyama West continue to be wild animals and although they are habituated to our presence, most do not ever interact directly with humans. Rocket is exceptional in this regard. He does not hesitate to sit in side by side body contact with a person when it suits his purpose to do so. In fact, he will sit on a person if need be. The chowline feeding procedure provides the best opportunity to see Rocket acting in this manner, and it also provides the best opportunity for a dangerous interaction. There are other animals who are overly familiar with the people who feed them, but these animals can be easily displaced by any quick movement of the body, or by reaching out toward them to frighten them away. These are wild animals who will not tolerate being touched by a human hand. The normal response of the few who need to be displaced in this fashion, is to flee and possibly to threaten the person who tried to touch them. Rocket will almost automatically bite any person who touches him or indicates an intention to do so. He has not

Juvenile male from the Deko family. Nickname: Art.

yet delivered a serious wound, however this is a growing concern. He behaves unlike any other monkey in this regard. His fearlessness and overconfidence are winning him the support of most of the young males in the group. Rocket will very likely be central and high ranking some day, but at this point he is smart enough not to display impertinence around any of the current high ranking central males.

The individual personalities of the monkeys are an indisputable reality for those who watch (and deal with) them, and personality is an important variable affecting behaviour patterns. The relatively consistent effects of kinship and dominance rank on behaviour will be mitigated by the personality characteristics of the individual, and in some cases the effects of a strong personality will override them. Many more examples of individual monkey personalities are presented throughout the book.

5

Age and the Life Course

Kinship, dominance, and personality have been described as major variables explaining the social behaviour of Japanese monkeys. A fourth variable which helps to explain variation in behaviour is age. This chapter explains the life course of the Japanese macaques in Texas and how social behaviour changes with age.

INFANTS AND THE BIRTH SEASON 🐾

Babies are born in the spring, usually in the months of April, May, and June. The seasonal pattern of mating in the fall and giving birth in the spring is consistent for macaque populations living at a variety of latitudes around the world. Births take place in the predawn hours but we have not had the opportunity, in Texas, of observing labour and delivery. A daily census of all adult females in the group reveals which females have given birth each day, thus providing the exact date of birth and identity of every new group member.

New mothers usually appear fully recovered only hours after the birth, even though they may have bloody fur and a placenta still attached to the baby. Some primiparous (first time) mothers are nervous and watchful for the first day or so, but the majority are multiparous and do not exhibit any obvious change in behaviour.

Infants are born with a coat colour considerably darker than that of any adult. Dark brown to black in colour, a newborn does not leave its mother's body for the first few days but clings to her ventrum during locomotion and stays cradled in her lap when she sits to eat or socialise. At first it seems to be permanently attached to the nipple, although it is not always actively suckling. But by the second week the infant has begun to venture off its mother's body to explore the area immediately around her. Most mothers do not permit the infant to go more than several centimetres away in this early stage. As weeks go by, the infant spends considerably more time away from its mother's body, often sitting up to a meter away. There is great variation in the "permissiveness" of the mothers. As indicated in Chapter Three, low ranking mothers tend to be more restrictive of their infant's movements, high ranking mothers more permissive. There are also individual differences and differences based on age. An

61

Infant riding jockey style.

experienced multiparous female is less likely to behave in an overly protective manner than is a first time mother.

REACTIONS TO A NEW BABY ⁊

Reactions of the rest of the troop to the new baby are muted. Only close friends and family have an opportunity to look at the new baby because they are the only ones in proximity under normal circumstances. In some species the birth of a new baby is cause for great excitement among most troop members, but not in Japanese macaques. Nearby animals may appear interested, but their behaviour is best described as "interested nonchalance" or "studied indifference". Instead of approaching the mother and looking directly at the baby, other animals, mostly females, will sit very close by, looking anywhere *but* at the baby. Increased frequency of these kinds of approaches, with the approacher sitting in a position and location that provides the opportunity to glance at the infant, suggests that there is an underlying interest in the new troop member.

This manner of expressing interest in something new has been observed in other instances as well. When a new climbing structure, for example, is erected in the enclosure, it will at first be surrounded by monkeys who are obviously *not* looking at it. Eventually they will approach and sniff and lick and generally become familiar with such a structure, ultimately using it for its intended climbing purpose. The closest kin of a new mother, generally her

Three week-old infant with distinct natal coat.

mother or another daughter, will be the first to get a good look at the new baby by offering grooming to the new mother. The groomer will "nonchalantly" groom increasingly close to the baby, and even actually touch the baby and begin to groom its tiny hands or feet. Most new mothers do not permit this actual touching of the new baby, even by a trusted family member, and respond by walking away from the groomer. To an observer familiar with the animals and their behaviour, the interest in the new baby is obvious. Interest in new babies is stronger early in the birth season when neonates are still relatively rare. Late in the birth season, the novelty of newborn infants seems to have worn off for most animals.

RESPONSE TO INFANT DEATH ⮿

A small number of miscarriages, still births, and neonatal deaths occur each spring, with varying reactions. Occasionally a stillborn infant is found in the area where the troop sleeps, without our ever knowing who gave birth to it. The adult females give no physical or behavioural clues that suggest a birth has taken place. More commonly the female carries the dead baby for several days. The hot south Texas climate, even in the spring, encourages rapid decomposition of the body. By the end of the first day this object may become unpleasant by human standards. Nevertheless, some monkey mothers will carry and protect it for days to come.

In late February of 1986, a young female who had been in estrus for the first time during the preceding mating season miscarried a fetus estimated to be two-thirds of the way to full term. (Gestation for Japanese macaques is normally about five months). This young female, #335, is the sister of Rocky. At that time, her social network included her mother, her older sister, and several juvenile members of the family. The appearance of this dead fetus seemed to confuse #335 considerably. As the event was outside of the normal birth season, there were no other new babies in the group. She carried the body around for several days, during which time her behaviour and that of her close contacts in the group altered. She herself was very protective of the carcass, even after it had decomposed to an unrecognisable mass. She would swing the carcass up onto her back and walk with it draped over her shoulders. Or she would run dragging it by the leg. Her family appeared to be quite put off by the malodorous object being dragged about by #335. Several times I saw her approach her older sister, Rue, for social contact or grooming, but Rue responded by running away. This was strange behaviour because usually the others ignore a dead baby even if the mother is carrying it around. Rue behaved as though she were frightened. Possibly the fact that it was not birth season had something to do with Rue's reaction. Or possibly the odd behaviour of #335 combined with the presence of the carcass led to the reaction. This strange response from her sister served to further confuse and produce odd behaviour in #335.

Whenever we spot a female with a dead baby we follow her hoping to retrieve the carcass for autopsy before decomposition progresses too far. With #335, we continued to follow because of the interesting behaviour patterns that were unfolding even after the fetus was past the point of being suitable for autopsy. On the sixth day after the miscarried fetus was first spotted, it disappeared, and within two or three days #335's behaviour and the interactions within her family group returned to normal. The possibility that hormonal fluctuations influenced the behaviour of #335 herself cannot be ruled out.

PLAY GROUPS ❦

In the first year of life no obvious sex differences in behaviour are evident. During this year infants begin to make social contact with other infants and with older siblings. An infant may find itself carried off by a zealous would-be alloparent, most commonly an older but still juvenile sister. During the first three to four months infants do not normally travel any distance from their mothers—they experiment with social interactions while still in close proximity to their mother.

I once came upon a very odd scene during the summer months, a scene which can only be described as an infant mob. Infants do not usually band together into big groups, at most forming small groups of two or three individuals playing in the immediate vicinity of their mothers. I was surprised by the

Two juveniles play wrestling. Play faces are evident.

size of this group of perhaps 25 black infants, no more than a few months old, jumping on one another and moving forward along the roadway. No adults were in direct association with the infants. The gang of infants came upon a yearling almost twice the size of any of them. What the infant gang did next can only be described as mobbing—they surrounded the yearling and began jumping all over it. It was impossible to see exactly what they were doing, although based on the response of the yearling they may have been pinching and biting. The yearling tried to escape, screaming defensively all the while. The mob of infants managed to prevent the yearling's escape for perhaps 60 seconds, after which it fled, far away, apparently traumatised. The incident had a comical appearance to me, but the yearling did not respond as though this were play behaviour. The baby mob then moved into the brushes near the waterholes and into a small tree. With 25 infants sitting in one small tree, it looked heavy, as though with some kind of large dark fruit. I stared at this remarkable scene for several minutes until the mob gradually disbanded.

I witnessed a similar phenomenon only once again, but the group was not as large and did not move around in an organised manner, being more like a very large play group. The potential mobbing behaviour of infants was fascinating, but one which I could not explore further because of its rarity of occurrence. In particular the absence of the mothers is puzzling. During the writing of this book, Lou reported from Texas that she had just witnessed a similar event. She went around a bush up onto the hill near the water holes and came upon a gang of as many as *50* infants sitting in and around a bush. She stared in disbelief for several seconds, wondering what would happen if a

As weeks go by, the infant spends considerably more time venturing away from its mother's body.

predator came along, and why the mothers were not present. There were no adults within view. As she pondered the predator question she took a few steps forward to look for any adults nearby when suddenly she was charged by Fang, the second ranked male in the group. He ran at her making full visual and vocal threats and causing her to stumble backward in surprise. In response to this commotion the mob of babies scattered.

WEANING AND THE INTERBIRTH INTERVAL 🍂

For Japanese macaque infants, weaning can begin any time after six months of age. Complete weaning from mother's milk may not be complete for some juveniles until 18 months of age, although by this time they are not babies any more. The normal pattern of reproduction is for each female to give birth every other year. Generally, infants do not have to deal with their mother's engaging in consort behaviour when they are only six months old. She returns to estrus when the offspring is 18 months old, and by then it is spending much of its time away from her. At the site in Texas however, food is plentiful and the every-other-year pattern has collapsed for some females into an interbirth interval of only one year. It is interesting that a life history characteristic such as the interbirth interval can be altered over a short period of time in response to changed environmental circumstances. The shorter interbirth interval allows

From birth to approximately one year of age, male genitalia are readily visible.

females to take advantage of a plentiful environment and readily increase their reproductive success. However, a six month old infant whose mother is actively consorting does face some difficulties. The infant is still highly dependent and likely to be spending much of its time in body contact with her. It can find itself right in the middle of a mating pair, forced to deal with close proximity to an adult male. Mothers who come into estrus will often speed up the process of weaning. Infants are sometimes caught in the line of sexual aggression directed toward its estrous mother.

INFANTS AND ADULT MALES ❧

Adult male Japanese macaques have, for the most part, very little to do with infants. Most males do not have any direct contact with infants, and have few opportunities to interact with them. Should an infant be threatened by a predator or some other external threat, however, males become very protective. Summa was a male who, despite having strong affiliative relationships with a number of adult females, rarely interacted with the many infants who were often around him. His behaviour toward them suggested indifference. Yet the fastest that I ever saw Summa move was when an infant playing near the fence tried to climb it and grabbed hold of a hot wire. The infant seemed to freeze in place on the fence and began screaming in pain and terror. Before any other animal, including the mother, had a chance to react, Summa had reached the fence, climbed up on it without hesitation and plucked the infant from the wire. Still hanging on to the infant, he ran back away from the fence and sat down looking disconcerted—this occurred in 1982 and he may not have quite "figured out" the fence. That is, he may not have understood from exactly what danger he had saved the infant. He may well have responded primarily to the message conveyed by the infant's screams.

He then sat with the infant in his lap for a few moments. The mother was sitting nearby looking very fearful. She did not appear to understand what had happened and was probably more concerned with the fact that the alpha male had possession of her infant than about the danger from which her youngster had been rescued. Seeing the mother, Summa put down the infant and walked away. The female then dashed in, collected her offspring, and quickly left the area for the safety of the bushes. I was surprised and impressed with Summa's performance. I had not predicted such heroic behaviour on his part particularly when the infant's mother (not a member of Summa's "inner circle") was nearby, and given that the threat was ill-defined.

Not all cases of males behaving protectively toward infants are devoid of personal motives on the part of the male offering protection. In cases where infants are trapped for tattooing, the higher the rank of the mother, the greater the response of the rest of the troop, including the adult males.[12] The ease with which some low ranking infants are removed from the troop is almost pitiful, especially when the infant is alarm calling and the mother is trying desperately, without support, to retrieve her baby. It is possible that our trapping activities are perceived by the monkeys as something different from true predation; therefore I cannot comment on whether the pattern of male protection of infants from predators would follow a similar pattern.

Japanese macaques are not one of the primate species for which male infanticidal tendencies in the wild have been reported. In the normal social setting males are not a danger to infants. In all cases with which I am familiar, infants which have been injured or killed by males have been the recipients of male aggression directed at the mother. Infants are vulnerable and those that get caught in the middle of an adult male attack upon an adult female may be hurt and even killed, but this is rare. However, there may be greater potential for male violence toward infants than is permitted in the normal social setting, with tightly bonded females always ready to form alliances against males. This is suggested by the fact that when we are involved in trapping and tattooing, we

---

12 Described further in chapter 6

temporarily remove animals from the safety of their normal kin based social milieu, and under these circumstances some females and their infants have been the target of vicious attacks by the peripheral males.[13]

On a more positive note, some males have been known to be very nurturant toward infants, playing with them, carrying them around, and protecting them from in-group squabbles, just as the mother would. Rheus6271 (Fatboy) was such a male. Over the years he developed "maternal-like" relationships with a number of different offspring. In the case of Rheus6271, special circumstances prevail. He was involved in a year-round close relationship with Cross-eyed Matsu which included consortships during mating season, and most of the infants toward which he directed this care-giving behaviour were her offspring. In other words, they may well have been his offspring. Even without going so far as to speculate on paternity, one cannot say that the relationships between Fatboy and Cross-eyed Matsu's infants are independent of the relationship between Fatboy and Cross-eyed Matsu herself.

Several of the adult males in the troop have shown such nurturant behaviour towards infants—that is, have formed strong bonds with specific infants—at one time or another, but this is not something that all males do. Indeed, many males may live out their lives without ever interacting in a nurturing way with an infant. The general tendency of most males to be indifferent to infants leads us to question the motives of those males engaging in this somewhat unusual behaviour,[14] and generally to assume that they have an ulterior motive. "Now what do you think he is up to?" is the question we invariably ask when we see this behaviour.

This perspective may be slightly cynical. There is good evidence that males are fully capable of providing weaned infants with competent care. Adoption of orphaned infants (those old enough to survive without mother's milk) by adult males are known from this and other species. Lack of opportunity to demonstrate these parental capabilities may explain the rarity of the behaviour under normal circumstances.

EMERGING SEX DIFFERENCES: THE PERIPHERAL MALES ✒

In the female bonded Japanese monkey society, which is characterised by male dispersal and female philopatry, males and females have very different life course patterns and very different life histories. By the age of two, males and females begin to diverge along these very different pathways. While females continue to interact primarily within the kin group of their mothers, males begin to break these ties and to forge new ones outside the realm of the the kinship network.

---

13 Described further in chapter 6.

14 See the discussion of Rocky and some infants from the Betta5966 lineage in chapter 3.

The peripheral male group, which "orbits" the main troop, becomes home to most adolescent males. Here they interact with other males of all ages. The peripheral male group includes not only adolescent males—adult males often spend a good portion of their lifetimes in the peripheral male group. The peripheral males are most appropriately viewed as a subgroup of the main group, and not as a separate all-male troop. Their movements are determined largely by the movements of the main troop. During mating season this male subgroup moves physically closer to the main troop, and mating between peripheral males and unrelated or distantly related central females is not uncommon. Occasionally a young female will become a temporary member of this subgroup, spending most of her time with these males. Once they begin to reproduce, these females usually adopt a more characteristically female pattern of behaviour and social interaction.

Mortality for males in the peripheral male group is very high. Many disappear—presumably they die and the carcass is not discovered. Others emigrate, and again, mortality for such males is probably the norm.

THE TRANSITION TO ADULTHOOD—MALES ❧

The transition to adulthood is much more gradual for males than it is for females. Males break the matrifocal bonds and become independent of the mother as early as age two or three. They begin to imitate mating behaviour at age three or four, and to engage in "real" mating behaviour at age five or six. By this time they are producing sperm. Yet, a six-year-old male neither looks nor always acts like an adult male. From age five until eight or nine he can best be described as subadult, not yet full-grown, and having behaviour patterns somewhere in between that of a juvenile and that of an adult. Many males do not reach skeletal maturity—their full height—until ten or 11, and after that they may still have some "filling out" to do.

This comparatively protracted transition to full adulthood, is followed by a life of group transference, in which new relationships and new social positions are continually being established. In Texas, mortality for these males has not been curtailed by the different environment, and a relatively small proportion of the males born in the group actually become fully adult males. The oldest males in the Arashiyama West Colony are all members of the central troop, although in the past there have been one or two males who have lived out long lives as peripheral members of the group. It is possible that some wander around the area as solitary animals.

THE TRANSITION TO ADULTHOOD—FEMALES ❧

The lives of males and females are also very different in the nature and extent of their social role changes. Because of kinship, the lives of females are

Peripheral males in a denuded mesquite tree.

Infant riding side-saddle.

Lady Di with her infant during watermelon season.

more uniform and their social networks more stable and unchanging over time. However, within this relatively smooth life course is one fairly abrupt transition—the transition to adulthood. At age two, a female Japanese macaque is a juvenile, still playing in and around her mother's social group. At age three she is still combining juvenile behaviours with imitations of adult behaviour. Adolescent females are commonly alloparents or aunts, mimicking maternal behaviour with any infants they can get access to. At four and one half years of age, most females experience first estrus, and for the first time must venture outside of the safety and security of the matrifocal unit. At age five most females give birth, and overnight are transformed from a nulliparous (not yet given birth) subadult to an adult, in the role of mother. From here on, it is basically more of the same in a life course characterised by continuity in adulthood.

CONTINUITY IN THE LIFE COURSE OF ADULT FEMALES ✌

In 1985 I began collecting data for my dissertation project on old age in female Japanese macaques. I was specifically interested in the social manifestations of old age—what was the behaviour and social role of old females compared with those of younger adult females? For over 20 years the social gerontology literature had been dominated by disengagement theory which predicted that in humans, old people would experience a withdrawal from the social world, and increased social isolation. The idea that old people are socially isolated is fundamental to popular perception, at least in North American society. Some of the early reports on old monkey behaviour had suggested that old monkeys might also experience a reduction in sociability and an increase in social isolation. Beyond this, little had been said about old monkey behaviour.

In my study,[15] I found no significant changes in female behaviour that could be linked to old age. Social isolation was observed in a small number of old females, but this could be explained by the absence of the normal kinship based social network of females. Recall Ranny, an old female, who was quite isolated and peripheral largely because she had never had any daughters survive to adulthood and was the only remaining female in her lineage. Similar circumstances of social isolation were observed in young females who were without a matrifocal unit (these cases are discussed in the chapter on kinship).

The absence of any significant changes in social behaviour in old females—given the relative continuity in their social lives past the attainment of adulthood—led me to think about how and why their lives are so different from ours in this respect. In all human societies, in spite of great cultural variation in the social manifestation of old age, the aged are recognised as a social group, with certain kinds of differential behaviour, social interactions, and social roles. What features of human lives and experiences cue the onset of this time of life in human societies—features that were absent in these monkeys? Three relevant distinctions between monkeys and humans were identified.

The first distinction between old monkeys and old humans pertains to reproduction in old age. The old female macaques in Texas continued to give birth to infants until the end of their lives. There was no post-reproductive cohort of female monkeys as there is of women in every known human society. Herein was a major distinction—elderly human females are no longer producing infants and when this primary role as mothers of dependent offspring has passed it is replaced with other kinds of behaviour and with other social roles. For the monkeys this change does not occur—they continue to nurture dependent offspring until the end of their lives—and this obviously plays a major role in the continuity observed in the adult life course. Several people have suggested to me that if the monkeys lived longer then we might see such a post-reproductive phase of life, and indeed this might be true. Likewise, if they had wings, they might fly. The fact is that they don't. The vast majority of Japanese macaque females do not live past their reproductive lifespan. Their lifespan and their reproductive lifespan are essentially the same. This is actually much easier to understand than is the human pattern of all human females ceasing to reproduce well in advance of the end of the maximum lifespan of our species,

---

15   For the full report on the study and the results see Do Old Female Monkeys Have a Specific Social Role? Primates 31(3): 363-373, July 1990 and Sociability in Female Japanese Monkeys: Human versus Nonhuman Primate Aging. American Anthropologist 93:588-598, 1991.

which is somewhere around 100 years.[16] This is not to say that there are not individuals who are very old and who have not had a baby in several years. Individual cases of exceptionally long lived macaque females who are no longer reproducing are known, but these are the exceptions which prove the rule. At the population level, the vast majority of females reproduce until the end of their lives. Keep in mind that the environment of these Texas monkeys, with light predation and plentiful food, would be expected to produce the longest lived individuals possible.

The second major distinction has to do with dependence and independence. Central to human gerontology is the concept of dependence, or loss of independence, in old age. Whether because of a departure from the workplace due to retirement, or because of increased frailty or failing health, loss of independence occurs among the aged more often than among other age groups. A monkey never loses its independence because it is not, once it has been weaned, ever truly dependent to begin with. A weaned monkey is never dependent on another monkey to help feed it and keep it alive. Except in very rare circumstances, monkeys do not gather and then share food. They do not engage in production and exchange. Each animal feeds itself and only itself. An animal who loses the ability to do so simply dies and is thus removed from the social world. A change in the social behaviour of old animals due to loss of subsistence independence does not occur. Likewise, as is clear from chapters two and three, because of the kinship basis of dominance, old females do not fall in dominance rank. This too is normally constant across the life course.

The final factor which I see as distinguishing the lives of old monkeys from the lives of old humans has to do with an awareness of mortality. Although this is very difficult to demonstrate, monkeys do not appear to be aware of their own mortality. I have seen no recognisable evidence (or I have not recognised the evidence) that monkeys have a conception of themselves—that they are objects unto themselves—and that they know themselves to be a temporary part of a universe that is more than them.[17] If they did know, as we do, that in old age they are nearing the end of a temporary existence, then this stage of life might be accompanied by some changes in behaviour. But in the absence of an individual or collective conscience to give meaning (or try to give meaning) to the end of the life course, it might just go unnoticed.

---

16 For a full discussion of menopause in a primatological and evolutionary perspective see M. S. M. Pavelka and L. M. Fedigan, Menopause: A comparative life history perspective. Yearbook of Physical Anthropology. 34:13-38 (1991).

17 The question of what goes on in the minds of animals is fascinating, and some very creative and exciting work is being done in this area. For a recent review, see D. Cheney and R. Seyfarth, How Monkeys See the World, 1992.

6

Conflict

The social life of Japanese macaques is largely peaceful and harmonious, characterised by high levels of affiliation, co-operation, and social bonding. Nonetheless, it is not without conflict. Conflict is an unavoidable aspect of social life; each species has its own pattern of conflict, its own way of fighting, its own way of resolving disputes.

This chapter is about conflict—what it looks like, what kinds of situations lead to it, and how it is resolved. Behaviours which appear in situations of conflict are normally referred to as *agonistic* behaviours and these are the focus of this chapter.[18] There is also some consideration of behaviours which resemble *aggression* in which the intent of the actor is apparently simply to harm the recipient. The agonistic behaviour of these Japanese monkeys in their daily social lives, as well as some revealing situations in which aggressive or agonistic behaviour is observed in situations involving members of other primate species (*Cercopithecus aethiops* and *Homo sapiens*), are described.

DESCRIPTION OF AGONISTIC BEHAVIOUR: HOW JAPANESE MONKEYS FIGHT ❧

Conflicts among macaques can range from very mild to very severe, and involve a variety of individual signals. The basic threat face involves drawing back the skin around the eyes and staring intently at the other animal. This basic threatening stare is easily understood across different primate species, and visitors to the site are warned never to stare at, and certainly not into the eyes of, a monkey. In its mildest form the threat involves only a flash of the eyes. A very mild conflict may involve no more than one animal flashing a single threat face, without vocalisations, in the direction of another who does not return the threat and may respond by ignoring the threat face or walking away. Such a mild

18 See J.P. Scott 1974. Agonistic behavior of primates: a comparative perspective. Primate Aggression, Territoriality and Xenophobia. (R.L. Holloway, ed) New York: Academic Press, pp 417-434. And L.M. Fedigan 1991. Primate Paradigms: Sex Roles and Social Bonds. Chicago: University of Chicago Press.

Solo, an adult central male, bares his canines.

conflict may easily go unnoticed by human observers and other monkeys. A more serious threat face would be accompanied by an open mouth with teeth showing, and ultimately with an aggressive barking or woofing vocalisation. These various elements can occur in any combination, and are often grouped together into a single ethogram unit called the "threat face". This label lumps together threat faces of varying intensity.

The aggressive barking or woofing vocalisation can vary in frequency and in loudness, depending upon the severity of the conflict. The aggressive barking is heard from the animal that is on the offensive. In addition, there are vocalisations that occur in conflict situations which are given primarily in defence. An animal who has received a visual/vocal threat will often respond by sitting and screaming defensively. Defensive screaming often serves to bring the support of relatives and friends, so an animal who is defensively screaming one moment may follow up with aggressive barking the next if the conflict develops to the point where the animal gets support and thus goes on the offensive. The difference between defensive and offensive vocalisations is obvious even to a relatively untrained human observer.

If the conflict reaches the point where visual and vocal threats are being exchanged by two animals, they will almost certainly be on their feet, lunging at one another and\or standing with a rigid straight-leg posture. At this point, the animals look around for support from other animals. In fact, if a dispute escalates to the point where it involves vocal and facial threats with chasing and lunging, others will very quickly be drawn into it. Each of the original opponents will seek the support of others nearby, and family members back one another. An animal joining the fight will almost always join in on the side of the animal to whom it is most closely related, at least maternally.

GETTING SUPPORT IN A FIGHT 🐦

The most notable characteristic of a Japanese macaque fight is that it tends to be noisy and confused, with several animals taking part, and little actual physical contact being made. Several animals may be barking and screaming and lunging and fleeing. Each side seems more interested in getting others to join in on their side than in actually attacking their opponents.

In order for a fight to reach this level of activity, the two sides would have to be fairly evenly matched. The highest ranking group of all, the family of Betta5966, rarely find themselves in this kind of protracted battle, because there are few circumstances in which the opponent(s) stand a chance. Fights involving the Betta5966 family are normally short because the opponents give up quickly. It is rare for Di to find herself needing Hatchet and Chunk and the others to help her—the certainty of their support is enough to prevent most others from challenging Di in the first place.

Only once did I see them involved in a "fair fight" and this took place when Hatchet was still alive. Di was sitting grooming her infant when another infant of about six months old approached. Di, obviously not wanting to be disturbed, flashed a threat face at the approaching infant. The infant began to scream, and in seconds the mother, a female named Adrienne, came charging out from behind a bush, threatening and lunging at Di. Di responded by screaming defensively, to bring out her family, and lunging at Adrienne. By now the infant was gone, but the fight was just beginning. Hatchet and Chunk joined in to support Di and Adrienne ran off a few meters. She then turned and screamed defensively at Hatchet and Di and Chunk, an action which brought the support of her mother, sister, daughter, and, most importantly, her "best friend"—Rocky. The next 30–40 seconds was a blur of monkeys lunging and screaming in a cloud of dust. Engima and Anne became involved, but the other side was motivated (the fight had started over an infant), and able to get powerful support. Without it, the fight would have ended in seconds. In the end it only lasted a moment or so, although such a battle can be frightening and seems to last much longer. It died down as quickly as it had arisen, with no actual physical contact being made, and it was not clear to me who won.

Despite these fairly consistent rules about who is likely to help whom, each fight is unique and the outcome is not always easy to predict. To what extent the fight escalates, and to what extent others become involved depends on everything from the mood and personality of each animal involved, to what the dispute is over, to interactions preceding the event that were not observed, and to a certain amount of chaos and chance. In some disputes in which several animals are implicated, the impression is that not every animal understands its role, or what the original dispute was about. Animal A may get support first from animal B, then from animal C, but as the situation escalates, animal C might turn and charge animal B. The several days of fighting during the 1974 takeover of the alpha female position by Betta5966 drew the attention of the alpha male, who altered the direction of his support in some irregular and puzzling ways.[19]

Physical contact does occur in fights among the macaques, but only in a very serious fight. In a scuffle that has escalated to involve chasing and lunging, contact aggression can follow. The animals may slap at one another, grab and pull fur, pinch, and finally pin down and bite the other animal. Some bites appear to be restrained by the biter, because wounds are not always apparent after the fact. Real bites do occur, however, and slashed flesh and deep canine punctures result, but often the biggest, noisiest, scariest fights involve no actual contact. "Hand-to-hand" combat is forestalled in this system of bluff charging, and support-getting; wounding may thus be less likely to occur in a big, noisy, polyadic fight. However, surprise attacks in which one animal proceeds directly to pinning and biting another, without involving any third parties, often result in serious wounds.

The big noisy fights that contain little actual contact are often over without a decisive victory. Indeed the multi-participant fight is often removed from the situation which originally provoked the participants. The outcome of a fight between two animals over a banana is much easier to determine—the one with the banana is the winner. When wounding occurs, one might argue that the more severely wounded animal is the loser. The best indication is when one side displays clear submissive signals, such as fear grimacing at the opponent. Much of the time it is not possible to identify a clear victor.

INTERSPECIES AGONISM: MACAQUES VS. VERVETS ❧

Species-specific patterns of behaviour are often highlighted when researchers have the opportunity to compare one species with another, or to observe the interactions between two different primate species. In one famous film clip, a very young chimpanzee is involved in a minor altercation with a much larger adult baboon. The baby chimp "wins" because it picks up a stick and swings it at the baboon, who shows no inclination to use such a weapon. This brief interspecies interaction plainly highlights some important aspects of both chimp and baboon behaviour. The opportunity to observe such interspecies interactions exists for those researchers whose subject animals share their range with one or more other primate species. This is common in many African and Asian locations. This opportunity does not exist, however, for those studying

---

19 See H. Gouzoules. 1980. A description of genealogical rank changes in a troop of Japanese monkeys (*Macaca fuscata*). Primates 21:262-267.

Japanese monkeys in Japan. Japanese macaques are sympatric with no other primate species except humans. The Arashiyama West Colony however, living in south Texas, shares its range with a small group of *Cercopithecus aethiops*, another old world monkey. This situation provides researchers with an unprecedented opportunity to look at the interactions of the two species, a situation which highlights species-specific behaviour patterns. Nowhere is this more striking than in the different ways in which these two species approach a fight.

The vervet group is small, its numbers hovering around 10 animals at any one time. The vervets maintain their spatial and social integrity, living alongside the macaques in their own social group. Interactions with macaques tend to be associated with conflict, such as in a dispute over a food source, or any time an infant is threatened by a member of the other species. Vervet monkeys are smaller than macaques. An adult male vervet is about the same size as a medium sized adult female macaque. Adult female vervets are the size of juvenile macaques. In the beginning, we were concerned that the vervets would be seriously wounded if they were to fight with the macaques, who are much bigger and more numerous.

When the vervets were first released, the macaque troop chased them away. The macaques were big, numerous, and vocally aggressive. The vervets, unfamiliar with the site, simply fled. After a time, however, the two groups came to accept one another, and to coexist. The vervets tended to range well away from the main macaque troop, separated by the peripheral males. Eventually, the peripheral males macaques became involved in a dispute from which the vervets did not flee, and the macaques were in for a surprise.

The two species display very different patterns of agonistic behaviour. The human managers had known all along that the likelihood of being bitten by a vervet was much greater than was the likelihood of being bitten by a macaque. For a macaque, biting is extreme and it does not happen often. Japanese macaque fights are characterised by chase and noise and show. Vervets, on the other hand, bite first and ask questions later. Their fights are not so much about bluff charging but about contact, and contact usually involves very sharp teeth. The macaques were unprepared for the fact that all of their barking, lunging and support-getting was lost on the vervets, who simply rushed up to the nearest macaque and sank their teeth into it. These species-specific differences in agonistic behaviour gave the vervets a real edge, and to this day they can always hold their own in a fight with the larger and more numerous macaques.

CAUSES OF CONFLICT: DIRECT COMPETITION FOR ACCESS TO RESOURCES ⚜

It should come as no surprise to learn that the level of agonism is highest at feeding time. When the feed truck first pulls into the enclosure, the animals gather for the food and, for the five to ten minutes it takes to scatter the provisions along the roadway, relative chaos and high levels of aggression occur. Hundreds of animals are running behind the truck, trying to get the choice food items. Two circumstances arise at this time. First, a highly desired resource is suddenly available from a localised source. This increases the tension caused by the intense desire of each animal to obtain this food. This drive may temporarily override each animal's "social sense". The established dominance hierarchy contains the chaos to some extent, but it does not entirely prevent the excitement and breakdown of some social rules at this time. This is the second circumstance taking place: a temporary breakdown of social order with all animal's rushing together, bumping into one another, each focused primarily on the food source, and perhaps momentarily forgetting who and where they are. Low ranking animals may find themselves reaching for a food pellet or a piece of fruit dropped from the truck only to discover Hatchet or Di or any number of other high ranking animals reaching for the same item. The higher ranking animal will direct aggression to the low ranking animal for impertinence as much as for access to the food item.

Thus, feeding time creates circumstances which result in high levels of inter-individual competition along with a temporary breakdown of the social rules that normally control the conflict that such competition produces. This situation would not normally occur in wild monkey populations which are not relying on human food enhancement for their diets. Nonetheless this situation

The troop feeds on eggplant that has been dumped from the truck. Eggplant is not a favorite and the troop is relatively calm.

**Ran68 charges aggressively at animal not in view. Female on right screams
defensively and assumes a submissive position in response. Animal in the
background watches.**

does bring behaviour patterns to light and make them more evident and salient
for the observers. Most behavioural researchers do not collect data at or near
feeding time, unless the research question directly pertains to agonistic behaviour and the research design permits the collection of data from artificially
induced conflict situations to reveal certain conflict behaviours. Within moments the truck has moved several hundred meters, scattering food along the
way, and the abnormal crowding, chaos, and aggression disappear.

A particular set of circumstances has allowed me to witness outright
competition for access to a localised and desired resource, but without the
crowding chaos that accompanies daily provisioning. When the animals were
first moved to the site near Dilley someone decided to put two domestic geese,
named Zeek and Fanny, into the enclosure to live in the ponds. The monkeys
and the geese co-existed peacefully for the most part. At first the monkeys,
particularly the juveniles, harassed the geese, but as anyone who has ever been
around domestic geese knows, these animals can take care of themselves. (After
12 years of research at the site I have never been bitten by a single one of the
400 monkeys. On more than one occasion I have been bitten by the geese).

The ongoing conflict involved the ill-fated eggs which Fanny continued
to lay and which the monkeys continued to find. After the initial battle between
the geese and the monkeys, the latter had possession of the large goose egg;
then began the conflict among the monkeys for access to the egg. Younger
animals were most interested in the egg, which changed hands several times as

higher and higher ranking individuals took control of it, running on three legs while holding the egg in the fourth. Sometimes the seizing of the egg would lead to threats and defensive screams and the families of the participants would be drawn into battle even if they were not interested in the egg. Amazingly, the egg would change hands several times and be transported a fair distance before finally being dropped to the ground and smashed. Zeek and Fanny never did succeed in having a family.

DOMINANCE INTERACTIONS AS CONFLICT 🔊

Aggressive behaviour is seen in a variety of contexts in the Japanese macaques, the primary ones being those that involve conflict between two animals which have incompatible or opposing needs or drives. Conflict due to the unavoidable competition over resources in daily life explains much of the aggressive or agonistic behaviour observed among the monkeys. However another related source of conflict involves dominance interactions. As described above, the dominance hierarchy represents a stabilised framework for keeping daily competition under control, providing stability and predictability in daily access to resources. Therefore, violations of appropriate dominance behavior, or a challenge to the existing hierarchy, may themselves be viewed as indirect conflict over access to resources, even if the interaction does not involve an obviously contested resource.

Both of the previous examples involve unusual or rare circumstances, however. Conflict over access to a desired and limited resource does occur in normal day to day life, but such conflict is expressed and/or resolved via the established dominance hierarchy. Shade is at a premium in south Texas in the summer, and there is insufficient cover in the enclosure at the site near Dilley. The dominance hierarchy normally determines who gets to have access to choice shady spots in the hot afternoon sun, and higher ranking animals can normally displace lower ranking ones from a given location simply by approaching. There may be an exchange of conflict signals, depending on the circumstances. As you will recall from Chapter Three, a host of contextual variables will affect the outcome of a dominance interaction. Nonetheless, a challenge to the existing dominance hierarchy through a failure to let a higher ranking animal go first to a resource, or a failure to vacate a desired location upon the approach of a high ranking animal, will usually lead to agonistic behaviour.

Once I was conducting a focal animal session on a Matsu female as she sat in the shade under a bush, when Hatchet approached. The moment that Matsu saw Hatchet coming, she fear grimaced and moved away from the area. Hatchet seemed to think this appropriate—she ignored Matsu and took the shady spot for herself. A failure on Matsu's part to accept and acknowledge Hatchet's priority of access would have constituted a conflict and resulted in an agonistic interaction. At the very least Hatchet would have threatened and chased Matsu.

Fatsu Matsu gives a threat face.

Was it possible that Hatchet was not intending to displace Matsu, but was actually approaching with the intent of affiliating? Was she perhaps looking for a grooming partner? Certainly it is possible, but it is highly unlikely. First, a Matsu female is a very unlikely social interactant for Hatchet. Second, to almost any individual other than those in her own family, Hatchet would need to give reassurance signals—a lip quiver or a warble—in order to have her intentions known. Without such signals it would be unwise for the other animal, especially a low ranking one, not to indicate acceptance of Hatchet's status. To do otherwise would constitute, or could be construed as, a challenge to the existing dominance relationship.

Sometimes aggressive behaviour from one animal to another is observed when there is no obvious competition for access to a desired resource. Sometimes it seems that the subordinate animal either has found itself in the wrong place at the wrong time, or has failed to direct the necessary submissive signals to a higher ranking animal, and thus by failing to acknowledge acceptance of the relationship the subordinate may be perceived as challenging the higher ranking animal.

The giving of submissive signals to indicate acceptance of another animal's higher rank is apparently not necessary all of the time. Certainly animals of similar rank, such as members of the same family, do not spend their days fear grimacing at one another. But when the animals involved are not of similar rank in the troop, an exchange of signals of dominance and submission is common.

UNPROVOKED AGGRESSION? ❧

It is not always clear why a particular conflict has occurred. One day I was collecting focal animal data on an old, fairly high ranking female, Rotte63. The session was calm and uneventful. Rotte had been sitting quietly being groomed by her yearling. After about 12 minutes of this, Rotte63 left the yearling, walked a short distance to the water hole and took a drink, then went out into the field and sat and ate some dirt.[20] After this she walked to a bush and sat down and began to groom herself. I did note in the comments column of the data sheet that Hatchet, Di, Enigma, and some of their offspring were about 10 meters away, but did not note this to be unusual, as Rotte63 was a high ranking central animal who occasionally had grooming bouts with members of the Betta 5966 family. For well over five minutes, Rotte63 sat peacefully grooming the fur on her leg. Suddenly and unexpectedly, Di charged and attacked Rotte63. The attack was sudden and unprovoked. She rushed up to Rotte63, grabbed and pinned her down, and bit her several times while making aggressive vocalisations. Rotte63 appeared to be as shocked by this attack as I was in observing it. She was certainly high ranking and central enough to have been sitting in close proximity to Di's family. Because my focus had been on Rotte63, I did not see what had transpired among the Betta5966 family immediately before this attack. No one came to Rotte63's aid, although she responded to the attack by screaming defensively and looking for support. Di calmly walked back to her group. Hatchet responded by turning and threatening Rotte63, who by then had had enough. She stopped screaming and walked away, putting at least another 10 meters between her and the Bettas before sitting down again. She did not resume her self-grooming, but remained watchful and vigilant, nervously looking around.

Had Rotte63 violated some subtle social rule of which I was not aware? Should she have paid some kind of tribute to Di and her family upon entering the area, and failed to do so? Had she been the innocent victim of redirected aggression following a conflict among the Bettas? This was not the first time that I longed to be able to ask questions of my silent subjects.

AGONISTIC SIGNALS AS SOCIAL MANIPULATION ❧

Japanese macaques use agonistic signals to manipulate a social situation. For example, it is not uncommon for an animal to "pick a fight" with another because it has looked around and realised that potential support is nearby.

---

20 It is not uncommon for animals to make a foray into the field to an area of ground that has been dug open by other monkeys and eat a small amount of dirt. It is assumed that some minerals are ingested this way.

Cross-eyed Matsu was regularly observed taking liberties, such as trying to grab choice food items, when Fatboy was present. In his absence she was very cautious—behaving appropriately for a very low ranking individual. Many animals have been observed using such manipulation. For example, I observed a low ranking female named Sissy sitting peacefully under a tree, with a low ranking Matsu mother and daughter pair. For a period of over 10 minutes I observed no interaction between Sissy and the Matsu pair. A male with whom Sissy spends a great deal of time, Pelka70, walked into the area and sat down. Sissy looked at Pelka70 and at the Matsu pair, then suddenly started screaming defensively at the Matsus and looking repeatedly in Pelka70's direction for support. Obliging her, he began to lunge and bark at the Matsus, who returned the threats but then fled. Pelka70 and Sissy then sat down for a grooming bout.

HUMAN/MONKEY AGGRESSIVE INTERACTIONS ❧

The first time that I drove up to the site of the Arashiyama West colony of Japanese macaques I was very excited about the prospect of coming face to face with animals of this famous colony. We were not, however, allowed to go directly into the enclosure. First we were given a lesson in "monkey etiquette". We were reminded that these were wild animals among whom we would be walking freely. This species was not known for its aggressiveness but the fact remained that we could get ourselves into a conflict with a monkey. I remember various bits of the lesson. Do not stare intently at an animal, try to appear nonchalant. Never look straight into a monkey's eyes. Do not try to touch an animal. Do not try to get too close—use binoculars to read tattoos from a distance of at least a few meters. Do not bring food into the enclosure. If you do get into a conflict with a monkey, remember that every animal out there is more closely related to the monkey than it is to you—285 other monkeys would join in to support their own.

None of this meant all that much to me at the time; I had no fear of these animals. They did not look dangerous to me in any video footage I had seen, and I was so anxious to get out and be among them that I just wanted this "etiquette" talk to be finished so we could get on with it. We broke up into small groups to walk into the enclosure, and my first sightings of the monkeys were thrilling. Soon we were in among them, watching the social groups, and trying to read tattoos. I saw a few small fights, but nothing that made me feel that I was not safe. The threat faces, lunges, and chases were directed at the other monkeys and the participants in these squabbles ignored us, as we were told they would if we "behaved". The days passed and I felt increasingly confident and safe . . . cavalier even.

It was well into the second week of the field school before I had an experience which ended my complacency and overconfidence. It was not a serious incident (certainly not by my current standards), but its effect was long-lasting. I had decided to watch a female, #69, who had an infant a few weeks old. I watched her as she groomed another female, and I followed when she went out into the fields to forage. I stood watching for a while, and then decided to sit down, as she had been eating in the same spot for some time. This put me at her level, more or less, and I sat with my legs crossed, my elbow on my knee and my chin resting on my hand, staring in her direction. Suddenly, without warning, she made a lunge at me, with canines bared, making full visual and vocal threat signals. I was so startled I fell backwards before being able to stand up to run. I remember my heart pounding as though it would jump right out of my chest. After running a few meters I stopped to look back, and #69 was not even looking at me any more, but was walking away.

My reaction had startled a few other monkeys who were now leaving the area. It was over, it seemed, but I was deeply shaken. It is not easy to convey the feeling of having an animal suddenly turn wild and aggressive and to be on the receiving end of those aggressive signals. These signals suggested that she meant business, and I did not want to think about the potential follow-through. For several days after that incident I was frightened of all of the monkeys. Since that "attack" seemed to have been unprovoked, I felt that another could come at any time. I felt panic rising in my throat any time the monkeys became involved in a conflict among themselves, or anytime that I saw #69. I kept my distance from her, fearing that she would remember and come at me again.

This basically harmless incident helped me to realise that these are complex wild animals who cannot be taken for granted or treated with complacency, ever. I am no longer afraid of the animals—if one behaves properly, there is nothing to be afraid of. The lunge from #69 was not unprovoked as you might have guessed. I had followed too intently, sat down too closely, and stared at a mother with a new baby. I had probably been working up to the lunge for some time. She probably did not intend to attack, but rather to chase me away, which she was very successful in doing. For the most part, I am now able to keep myself out of conflict situations with the monkeys by remaining separate from their social world. The monkeys, however, are not able to keep themselves out of conflict situations with other monkeys, as conflict is an unavoidable element of social life, and a part of the daily lives of all of the monkeys.

Although the policy of the management is to keep human interference to a minimum, some handling of the animals is necessary. In the context of our manipulations I have witnessed aggressive behaviour directed at other monkeys, and at us, and some of these situations help to illustrate further the kinds of situations that result in aggression. I will begin by relaying the story of the most frightening experience I have ever had in dealing with these monkeys, an experience that made the lunge by #69 during my first days at the site seem laughably tame.

Any time that we have to trap animals, our status changes dramatically as far as the animals are concerned. Suddenly we become enemies and maybe predators. Few circumstances will provoke an aggressive response as effectively as will trapping an infant, particularly if that infant is high ranking. On several occasions Lou and I have trapped infant and juvenile members of high ranking families for tattooing, and have found ourselves facing large numbers of monkeys intent upon securing the safety of the infant (and/or winning points with the family of the infant). The challenge for us is to remove the juveniles and/or infants from the enclosure without having them, or us, injured.

In the early 1980's, an additional three hectares of brush was fenced off on the southwest corner of the enclosure. By this time it was clear that the original enclosure provided insufficient natural forage and cover, and it was hoped that the animals would spend some time in this annex to the enclosure. In addition, the passageway between the two parts of the enclosure was designed so that it could be used as a trap for large numbers of animals at once.

Unfortunately, the animals showed no inclination to use this new enclosed area of brush. When the time came to use the trap facility, we tried to lure the monkeys to the area and through the passageway, by scattering high priority food items, like bananas and grapes, in a line from the waterholes out across the field to the trap. A number of animals followed and ate the food, but when they reached the passageway refused to venture into it. We tried not feeding them for a day to increase their motivation, then sprinkled the regular food lightly across the field dumping the lion's share of it inside the passageway. A few animals went in to gorge themselves, but the high ranking central animals stayed out. We needed the troop leaders to venture through before the main body of the troop would follow.

In order to achieve this we focused our attentions on Hatchet. We tried unsuccessfully to entice her through the passageway with caramels, strawberries, chocolate, peanuts and avocados. We reasoned that we would have to find something that she cared enough about to forget her suspicions for a few minutes and enter the trap. Our intent was to let her go through, then trap a large number of the others that would follow. But what would Hatchet care that much about? What did we have that she wanted? Lou came up with an answer. She said we needed Hatchet's baby.

Later that day Lou and I were back in the enclosure with the box trap set, hoping to lure Hatchet's infant into the trap. This was the plan, although I am not sure why we thought it would work. The Betta5966 family was sitting near the trap, but as usual, Hatchet would not allow any of her juvenile offspring to venture inside. I was holding the rope which held the trap door, and Lou was standing a few meters away, watching the trap. After a time we became very discouraged. Lou was standing only a foot or so away from Anne, Hatchet's eldest daughter. The animals were accustomed to Lou's presence and ignored her. Watching, I saw Lou take a deep breath and stand up straight. Then, in a split second flash, she bent over and grabbed the dark infant which was sitting calmly beside its mother Anne. And the pandemonium began.

Anne began lunging at Lou, slapping her legs. The monkeys who had been in and around the trap fled when I released the rope, dropping the door. Lou began walking backwards across the roadway toward the field. Hatchet and Di were following behind Anne, but appeared not to know just yet what was going on—Lou had tucked the baby into her shirt and it was out of sight. Lou instructed me to stay calm and not to turn my back on the Bettas, who were becoming more agitated as Anne continued her screaming and lunging. Then, from inside Lou's shirt, the baby started to scream in distress.

At the sound of the baby in Lou's shirt, Hatchet and all of her daughters, realising now the situation, broke into frantic lunging and slapping and barking. Alarm calls were being given by several of the adults. Summa and Rocky appeared, canines bared. By now we were five or ten meters out into the field, and the gang that had surrounded us was growing by the second. Distant branches of the Betta family appeared. Then the Rottes. Then the Midoris. Then the Rheuses and the Dekos and the Memes. There were literally hundreds of monkeys, all barking and screaming. Several animals were lunging at us, slapping our legs and leaping on us. I was too frightened to even speak and was astounded to hear Lou say "It's working!"

I turned and looked across the field and saw that we had more than a hundred meters to go. "We can't make it all the way up there!" I yelled, unsuccessfully trying to hide the panic I felt. She responded with "Look, I think every single adult central male is here! I've never seen them all together like this!" How she could be making behavioural observations at a time like this was beyond me. Then Lou jerked as a large adult male threw his whole body weight against her back, grabbing hold of her clothes and shaking vigorously. I felt a sudden pain and looked down to see a female pinching my lower leg. Macaques do not pinch lightly and this was the kind of pinch that would leave a bruise. This warned me that we were getting closer to the point at which biting would occur. Lou was yelling "Back to back! Stay back to back! They won't attack if we're looking at them!" I knew this was true. Trouble was more likely to come up from behind, but this situation was now extremely dangerous and far beyond what I was prepared for.

Fortunately the ordeal ended a moment later. Hatchet jumped up and grabbed Lou's arm with all four of her feet, pulling Lou's hand, the one holding her infant grandchild, part way out of her shirt. Seeing the baby caused a whole new wave of lunges and slaps and pinches and full-body assaults. Instantly a Rheus female jumped up and grabbed the baby from Lou's hand. She ran full speed for two or three seconds with the baby, then dropped it and kept running. She had endangered herself by becoming that involved and for her troubles might have been attacked herself had she not quickly distanced herself from the infant.

That was certainly the most dangerous situation I have ever faced, a situation provoked by our sudden predatory behaviour involving a very high ranking infant. I had witnessed a troop attack on an ex-captive male macaque that we had released into the area a year before, and thought I knew what he must have felt that day. In neither case was any biting recorded. Note that these extreme situations were created by our manipulations, and that in the normal day-to-day life of these animals, they might never experience such a troop-wide attack or defence. Nonetheless, this is a behavioural potential which was revealed when the circumstances presented themselves.

Human interventions are kept to a minimum for a number of reasons, primary among them the desire to have the animals living as normally as is

Lou Griffin and Mary Pavelka. Once animals are caught, it must be ensured that they are suitable for immobilisation and processing.

possible for a provisioned troop of Japanese snow monkeys living in Texas. Also, the above example shows that interventions can be risky for the human managers. We were surprised to discover, early on, that manipulations of the animals could place them in grave danger from *their own kind*. When an animal has been trapped and/or sedated, that monkey's worst enemy at that moment may well be another monkey.

MONKEY/MONKEY AGGRESSION OUTSIDE OF THE NORMAL SOCIAL SETTING ❧

By the mid-1980's the peripheral males had established a normal ranging pattern which included the trees and brush north of the enclosure, the same area in which the researchers' trailers are located. Once we removed a trapped animal from the enclosure we brought them to this area for processing, and if the peripheral males were in the area at the time, we had to be extremely careful to protect the incapacitated animal from being wounded by these free-ranging males. When I first witnessed the deadly determination with which some of the peripheral males tried to injure a sedated animal, I was shocked by the serious, purposeful and persistent nature of the attacks. This behaviour was hard to classify as agonism—it did not appear to be a situation of conflict. One animal was totally vulnerable and helpless, and the other clearly intent upon doing it harm. High-ranking females were at the greatest risk.

In order to maintain individual identification of all animals, it is important that infants are trapped and tattooed while they are still young enough to be dependent on their mother. It is normal for a mother, or several mothers, to go into the trap with their youngest infant clinging to their ventrums. Both mother and infant are then sedated, giving us the opportunity to weigh, measure, inspect, and re-tattoo the mother. It is also in the best interests of the infant not to be separated from its mother for this procedure.

The first high ranking animal I ever helped trap was Enigma; I learned then how dangerous the peripheral males could be. When we loaded the trap containing Enigma and two other females, with their babies, into the truck, we faced the expected hair raising protests of Enigma's mother and sisters and friends. But we did manage to get out of the enclosure where *we* would be safe. Not so for Enigma and her baby, I learned. From the moment that we entered the area outside, two of the peripheral males were on the back of the truck, threatening Enigma and trying to reach into the cage to grab her or her baby. She was already traumatised (no sedative had yet been administered), but when she saw herself facing these males her behaviour suggested fear that far exceeded what she felt in relation to us.

Lou sat in the back of the truck, trying to keep the males away, and she found them to be *very* persistent. She had to resort to waving a shovel in the air. Her presence without the weapon was not sufficient to deter them. But the determined effort to harm Enigma and her baby was just beginning. While we were sedating her, and then while she was immobilised and being processed, the peripheral males took every opportunity to try to grab or bite Enigma and her baby. These same males would, in all likelihood, have taken part in defending them from us in the main troop. But outside under these different circumstances, they were the attackers. They tried every possible way of getting to the sedated Enigma. As I worked on her tattoo I noticed a hairy hand reaching up from below the table. I kicked at the animal under the table, and then called the dogs to sit by my feet to prevent a further approach from this direction. Instantly I discovered several males on top of the roof trying to reach Enigma from this position. They were prepared to try anything. No aggression was directed at the humans, as it would have been had these males been interested in protecting Enigma and the baby from us. They were single minded in their intent to harm and perhaps even kill this high ranking but now defenseless monkey pair.

Over the years I have gained enough first-hand experience with this situation, and discussed with Lou the many additional ones that she has faced, to be certain of two regularities in this behaviour. First, the very highest ranking females are those who receive the most severe and persistent agonistic attacks by the peripheral males. Any animal from the main troop is vulnerable to a peripheral male attack while removed from their normal social milieu, but none so much as the high ranking central females. Second, these males mean business, and the very lives of the main troop animals are in danger under these circumstances. We have now developed procedures to prevent injury, but while we were first coming to terms with this behaviour, a small number of serious woundings and one death did occur at the hands of the peripheral males.

What underlying behaviour pattern or potential is being revealed by these unusual circumstances? The regularities in the nature of this aggression suggest that the peripheral males know "who is who" in the centre of the troop. Why they are so intent to harm females with whom they would probably never interact under normal circumstances, and to whom they would most certainly have to defer if they did, is an intriguing question.

LONG MEMORIES AND ENDURING LOYALTIES ❧

I did, on another occasion, see evidence that the monkeys outside the enclosure continue to remember the animals inside. Matsu58 was an old female who had left the enclosure at age 24 and moved into the area with the peripheral males. (Matsu58 was introduced in chapter one). One day more than two years after she had left the troop, we were outside the enclosure tattooing some juvenile animals that we had trapped inside. The drug used to immobilise the animals is called Ketamine, and it can interfere with thermoregulation. If it is hot outside we must take precautions to prevent the anaesthetised animal from overheating.

On this occasion we had just tattooed a low ranking juvenile male from the central troop. I had entered on the data sheets that this was the offspring of Matsu5874. I did not make the connection right away between this juvenile and Matsu58 who lived with the peripheral males. We had had no trouble from the peripheral males during this session—the animals we were tattooing were mostly juvenile males and were not high ranking. The peripheral males showed no interest in harming them. Even if I had thought about the fact that this was old Matsu's grandson, I would not have expected any trouble from her—he would have been barely a year old when she left the troop, abandoning him along with the rest of her family. Yet as I carried this limp young male over to the water trough to soak him down I was ambushed by Matsu58. She charged me from behind and grabbed the backs of my legs, running bipedally to keep up with me while screaming and pinching my legs with her hands. Lou rushed in and chased off Matsu58 off and we quickly put the young male in a cage, safely out of reach. Given old Matsu's personality and past behaviour, we shook our heads in wonder that she would remember this descendant, and more so that she would bother to try to defend or rescue him.

ABNORMAL BEHAVIOUR AS A STIMULUS FOR AGGRESSION

It has long been noted by primatologists that abnormal behaviour in an individual invites aggressive attacks by other animals. The failure of an individual to behave appropriately in the social context constitutes a violation of the rules of normal behaviour. Males in particular respond to these violations by attacking the animal who is already the victim of some misfortune. In this troop of snow monkeys in Texas such abnormal behaviour is produced by illness and disease such as stroke or tetanus and by accidents such as electrocution.

Another consistent source of abnormal behaviour is anaesthesia produced by human manipulations. This occurs when an animal which appeared fully revived is released prematurely, or when an animal is darted and it receives enough of the injection to affect co-ordination but not enough to fully immobilise it. Such an animal will stagger and fall repeatedly. Even a mother will shake, threaten, and bite her offspring in this condition (as if to punish if for behaving improperly), but she will also protect it from others. An incapacitated animal is in the greatest danger when separated from the protection of the female kin group.

Interestingly, the intensity of the aggressive reaction (to an animal who is behaving abnormally due to anaesthesia) has lessened consistently over the years. Since trapping is done sporadically throughout the year, the animals have become more familiar with this behaviour pattern. While not an everyday behaviour, it is no longer unfamiliar enough to incite the aggressive response of novel abnormality.

Another situation in which I observed abnormal behaviour being met with aggression was due to an intervention, of sorts, but it did not involve trapping or sedation. Over Christmas,1989, my husband travelled with me to the site to assist with the trapping of females who were slated to receive contraceptive injections—by this time we began actively trying to control the birthrate. A particularly cold snap prevented us from engaging in trapping for several days. On one of these days Lou's husband, Frank, and my husband, Joe, volunteered to feed the monkeys. They returned several hours later with stories of how the waterholes were frozen over completely and the monkeys were playing on the ice, sliding around, and so on. Having never seen ice in south Texas I was dismayed at having missed this unusual monkey behaviour, and the next morning I set out bright and early. It was considerably warmer the next day, and we knew the ice would not last. Fortunately, when we arrived, the water holes were still frozen. Unfortunately, the monkeys were not playing on the ice. Perhaps the novelty had worn off. Determined to see monkeys in south Texas on an ice covered pond, I scattered peanuts across the ice. It worked, of course, and several animals rushed out to retrieve the peanuts, sliding around just as Joe and Frank had described from the day before. I stood on the edge of the pond and watched this unusual scene with delight. Then I became conscious of a strange creaking noise—one that I knew I had heard before, but could not recognise in that context. Seconds later, the entire middle of the pond collapsed inward and between 10 to 20 monkeys, many juveniles, were submerged in the icy water. They scrambled to get out, but the wet slippery ice made it very difficult. Larger animals had the additional problem of the ice breaking under them when they did manage to get on top of it. It took several minutes before they were all out, and a number continued to risk getting dunked by venturing out to the edge of the broken ice to grab the peanuts still floating in the water.

A large adult male, nicknamed Flaco decided to try his luck at getting some of the floating peanuts, but for him it was a mistake. Because of his weight, he broke through the ice before retrieving even one peanut, and was then unable to get out. He continually managed to scramble up onto the ice, only to have it break through beneath him. He appeared quite frightened—maybe panicked, because he began making a variety of agonistic vocalisations. The commotion of a few moments earlier had died down, and his thrashing and splashing and vocalising attracted the attention of first one, then another, and then several of the adult central males. His highly abnormal behaviour was met with aggression: a large group of males gathered on the edge of the pond vocalising aggressively at Flaco. As he frantically tried to escape the icy water and reach the shore, he now had a gang including most of the central adult males waiting for him with canines bared. This coalition of central males had apparently formed in response to Flaco's abnormal behaviour. When he finally did make it to the still-thick ice near the edge of the pond, he tried to run but repeatedly slipped on the wet ice, and this was met with a wave of more intense and aggressive vocalisations from the gang of males. Finding his feet on solid ground he broke into a full run, with the other males in pursuit. I did not see what happened to him after that, but the next day he had no visible wounds and nothing had changed with regard to his rank or status as a central male.

In this chapter I have tried to convey a sense of what conflict is like for this troop of monkeys. In attempting to provide an overview of the situations which create conflict or result in displays of aggressive behaviour, one major area has not been described. This is the mating season, which brings with it significant increases in aggressive behaviour towards females from males. Some of it results in serious wounding, and most of it appears to be unprovoked. I hesitate even to refer to this as agonistic behaviour, because no conflict between the animals is readily apparent. The presence of estrous females, however, should be listed as an additional situation or circumstance which leads to aggressive behaviour, and this is described more fully in the next chapter.

7

Sex

MATING SEASON 🙋

Japanese macaques are seasonal breeders, displaying sexual behaviour only at certain times of the year. Mating season occurs in the fall, beginning in late September or early October, and carrying through until late January or early February. A birth season follows in the early spring. This Japanese pattern of mating in the fall and giving birth in the spring is maintained in Texas. The onset of the mating season brings with it many changes in both individual and group behaviour making the demarcation of the seasons very obvious behaviourally.

Spring comes early in Texas, and March in particular is a wonderful time. Spring flowers are in bloom, the weather is warm and breezy, and the monkeys are calm. The troop is spatially dispersed, and life is peaceful and quiet. The birth of new babies is a source of interest to monkeys and humans alike, but is not associated with any discernible increase in excitement or activity. As the summer wears on, temperatures rise, reaching 100 degrees Fahrenheit by about 9:00 am in July and August. The monkeys spend much of their day lying in the shade.

In September, as the weather begins to cool down, activity picks up, and the mating season begins. The first indication that mating season is beginning are the courtship chases of males. Initially these are occasional events, perhaps one or two per day. Soon chases are an almost constant occurrence. At the same time, the troop is becoming more spatially consolidated. The peripheral males move in and become much more a part of the troop.

By November, mating season is in full swing and the whole troop is active. There is a general air of action and uncertainty. Males roam looking for females to chase. Females are watchful and nervous, as males seem to appear out of nowhere to launch a chase. Couples can be observed in various stages of courtship and mating. A new set of behaviours, not seen in the non-mating seasons, comes into play. A researcher watching mating season activities for the first time might take weeks to develop and modify an ethogram which includes all of these new behaviours.

ESTRUS ❧

In addition to the partitioning of all mating activity into one season is the fact that within this season, females are only interested in mating periodically. Females undergo periods of physiological change which are associated with clear changes in behaviour. During these times the female is said to be in estrus. It is only during estrus that a female will be motivated to approach males for mating, and it is only during estrus that females will receive advances from males. Estrus has been described as that period in which females may be motivated and/or willing to mate.[21] The concept of estrus corresponds roughly to the periods of "heat" that occur in female dogs and cats.

Estrus does not occur in a regular pattern. A female may show signs of being in estrus for one day, for three weeks, or anything in between. Furthermore, she may come into estrus many times, or only once during the mating season. Since all mating activity takes place when a female is in estrus, we assume that ovulation and conception also take place during this time but other than this general correspondence, there are few external indicators of the specific internal endocrine events. In some baboon species, physical changes associated with estrus are very regular and predictable, allowing researchers to pinpoint the exact day of ovulation based on external signs. This is not the case with Japanese monkeys, where there is no direct association that we know of between external signs and internal endocrine conditions.

Physical signs of estrus in Japanese monkeys in Texas include a red face and/or a red perineum. The perineum is the skin between the anus and vulva of the female, and between the anus and testicles of the male. This area of bare skin, often several inches across, is clearly visible when the animal is walking away. A slight swelling sometimes accompanies the reddening of this area, although the untrained eye might miss it (remember that the eyes that matter are the eyes of the other monkeys, and we must assume that they *are* trained). The colour of the face and the perineum are usually the same for any individual. Although estrus is a specifically female condition, males in the presence of estrous females may also undergo a reddening of the face and perineum. Even more obvious than these physical changes are the behavioural changes which accompany them. With estrus comes a whole new repertoire of behaviours exhibited by both females and males.

The estrus behaviour of female Japanese macaques involves both active solicitation of males, and the acceptance of advances initiated by males. Preconceived notions that the latter are more common are incorrect; active solicitation behaviours of the females toward males (proceptivity) are more striking and more common than are passive acceptance behaviours (receptivity) or active rejection behaviours. Four stages in female courtship of males (procep-

---

21 L.M.Fedigan. 1992. Primate Paradigms, Ch 10.

tivity) have been identified. They are first, advertising and monitoring; second, attempting to gain proximity to a specific male; third, attempting to initiate a mount series (copulation); and fourth, attempting to maintain a mount series.[22] The first two stages essentially involve the female attempting to get into a consort relationship with a specific male. The third and fourth stages take place once a female is in association with a specific male. Before describing these stages it will be useful to describe the consort bonds that characterise Japanese monkey sexual relationships.

CONSORTS ❧

A consort is an interesting sociosexual bond that forms in a number of primate species, particularly those which exhibit the series mounting copulatory pattern (see below). A mating pair enters into a prolonged relationship that involves much more than just sexual activity. For a variable period of time, the two will travel together, eat together, defend each other in fights, and generally act as a kind of social unit. This pair of animals will also engage in copulations any number of times throughout the day. It is not necessary to witness an actual copulation in order to be certain that two animals have entered into a consort. Although the mutual proximity, travelling, eating, and agonistic support are similar to what is seen in pairs of related animals who interact in the nonmating season, the behaviour of a consorting pair is also unique and distinctive in many ways. There is little chance that a researcher would confuse the friendly inter-actions of a nonmating adult male and female with a consort pairing, or the kinship interactions of two females with a female-female consort bond. The behaviour pattern of consort pairs of animals is distinct from that observed during the nonmating season or between a non-mating pair.

A consort lasts anywhere from a few hours to a few weeks. Some animals tend to engage in longer term consorts than do others. The length of a consort, or the amount of time that a female is in estrus, should have something to do with conception. But in fact good evidence exists to suggest that much estrus behaviour, courtship, and consorting takes place after a female has already conceived. This post-conception estrus behaviour is clearly not needed for reproduction.

When first studying this troop, I did not suspect that much of the consort activity went beyond the actual demands of reproduction. I assumed that fe-males who stayed in estrus for long periods of time, or came into estrus repeatedly over the breeding season, must be yet to conceive. At the start of the 1982 mating season I was told about a female, Kujiro69, who had been in estrus

---

22 G.R. Stephenson. 1973. Testing for group specific communication patterns in Japanese macaques. Symp. IV Congr. Primatol. Volume 1: Precultural Primate Behavior. Basel: S. Karger.

for the entire 1981 mating season. She had been very sexually active during this whole extended period. I assumed that she must have conceived late in the season. I was also given a birth list from the spring of 1982 that included all females who had given birth and the sex of the infant. This list was arranged from the first birth of the season to the last. One of the first mother's names on the list was Kujiro69. It took a few moments for me to realise the implications of this. There was no indication that the baby had been born prematurely. Obviously Kujiro had conceived very early in the previous mating season, and much of the activity in which she was involved was superfluous from a reproductive point of view.

FEMALE COURTSHIP STAGE ONE—ADVERTISING AND MONITORING ☙

Females who are in estrus can often be identified behaviourally even if they are not associating with a particular male. In the period before associating with a particular male, females, particularly young females, sometimes appear agitated and hyperactive. One such female was Petitemon6476, nicknamed "Tomboy" because she seemed to be following a more typically male life path. At age six she was associating mostly with the peripheral males rather than her matrifocal kin group. By August 1982, Tomboy had not yet shown any signs of coming into estrus, even though she was now almost six and a half, two years older than most females when they experience their first estrus. But she was not to remain a tomboy forever, finally coming into estrus during the 1982 season. At that time, Tomboy seemed genuinely confused by the changes in her body.

At first, she became very hyperactive. Following her was exhausting—she travelled nonstop and at a fairly good speed, staying away from any other animals. She appeared genuinely perplexed that her peripheral male associates were suddenly chasing her, and chose to stay away from them. Possibly she felt that she had been driven out. Then she began to make estrus vocalisations, calls heard only during mating season and only by females in estrus. When performed by a female not yet associated with a specific male partner, these vocalisations probably function as advertisement, but it is doubtful that Tomboy knew how to use them appropriately. She travelled around, sometimes sitting, sometimes moving, and estrus screaming the whole time. This brought on the predictable attentions of adult males, some of them from the centre of the troop. In spite of all the advertising, Tomboy behaved apprehensively, and did not appear to welcome any approaches from adult males. She seemed to be on the move partly to try to stay out of trouble. It was as though she was giving out "invitation" signals of which she was unaware and was frightened and confused by the responses.

At some level the male interest must have been welcome. She was, after all, clearly in estrus. But fear dominated her responses, at least initially. Young Tomboy had an advantage over many first-time estrous females in that she was older and more experienced in interacting with adult males. Thus, she came to terms fairly quickly with the changes in her body and those in her social interactions. Soon she was able to move into the next stage of female courtship, that of trying to establish contact with a particular male.

This first stage of advertising and monitoring is not exclusive to inexperienced females, it is just more noticeable in these females. Nulliparous (never been pregnant) females have not yet developed the skill of successfully engaging a specific male, hence the prolonged, exaggerated, and sometimes inappropriate display of estrus behaviours and use of estrus signals. Older females who are in estrus but not yet in association with a specific male are also advertising and/or monitoring, however they are calmer and more sophisticated in their use of the signals, tending to receive less aggression from males as a result. As discussed in the chapter on conflict, violations of normal or appropriate social behaviour usually provoke aggression, and the behaviour of these young females may be another example. First time estrous females receive more aggression, and more courtship chases that end in aggression, than do more experienced females. So while the inexperienced and sometimes exaggerated use of courtship signals was inappropriate, the fear of males was not.

ATTEMPTING TO GAIN PROXIMITY ❧

The first stage of active female courtship ends when the female begins to direct behaviours toward a specific male; in the second stage of courtship the female attempts to gain proximity to this male. The first thing that she will do is follow him. What factors led to her choice of a particular male is not known. She may have been the recipient of male courtship signals, but in very few cases did I witness this sequence of events. It is not possible to observe all the behaviours that may have been directed toward a female before her apparent choice of a particular male. Gray Eaton of the Oregon Regional Primate Centre once said, based on a sighting of a female-initiated contact with a male, that he may have "sent her roses a week ago".[23] It only becomes obvious to the human observer when one of the animals begins to follow the other one around. A female who follows a male around, instead of travelling with her own family group, is showing distinct estrus or courtship behaviour.

This stage of trying to gain proximity to a certain male is characterised mostly by following and sitting near him. First, the female will follow at a distance and sit a few meters away from the male; this distance will decrease as the courtship progresses. However, she must proceed with caution, as males often lunge aggressively or chase females who approach them too fast or too soon. This is an important stage in the formation of the bond between the two

---

23 G.G. Eaton. 1978. Longitudinal studies of sexual behavior in the Oregon troop of Japanese macaques.   Sex and Behavior. Status and Prospectus. (T.E. McGill, D.A. Dewsbury and B.D. Sachs, eds.), New York: Plenum Press, pp.35-59.

animals. Here they come to a mutual understanding and acknowledgement that they are entering into a consort together. It is at this time that the two animals are establishing the consort bond. The female follows the male around, and sits down near him whenever he stops moving. It is easy to see what male she is after, not only from her following and sitting nearby, but because she will be very obviously looking at him and watching what he does and where he goes. If the male remains stationary for more than a few moments, the female may try to decrease gradually the space between them. Since it is female courtship behaviour that is being discussed, in which the female is the primary initiator, the behaviour of the male is usually not that striking. He carries on his business and ignores her. The male is aware of the female's presence, and her intentions, so it might be that by simply not chasing her away he is beginning to co-operate. The female must be careful at this stage, because crowding the male is an apparent violation of social rules and may provoke an aggressive attack. This female is now travelling around after this male, and may not have the safety of her female kin network nearby to back her up and protect her.

Once the male has accepted the idea that this female will be following him around and sitting nearby (i.e. he has not chased her off), she may begin to inch herself closer to him when he has been stationary for a period of time. This inching closer can be amusing to watch, because the behaviour of the female suggests that she is trying to be nonchalant and inconspicuous, when to the researcher's eye the behaviour is very obvious. The female might be sitting perhaps 1.5 meters away, continually glancing at him. She quickly lifts her bottom off the ground, shifts over about 15 centimetres, and is still again. She then looks around, anywhere but at the male, with an air of indifference.

Again, one must assume that the male is aware of what is going on and is in compliance. This stage takes anywhere from 30 minutes to several hours, depending on the personalities and motivations of the individuals involved. This stage is complete when the female gets close enough to be sitting in body contact with the male. That last inch, the one that puts her in body contact with him, is nerve wracking for observer and (apparently) female alike, as one has the impression that she is taking a big chance with this final bold move. Fearfulness of the female is evidenced by a flinching, startled action occurring in response to any movement by the male. In other words, females, particularly lower ranking ones, act as though any movement might be the start of an aggressive reaction from the male, as sometimes it is. Fear grimaces at the male are also frequent. But after they have sat with fur touching for a short while, her nervousness may be replaced by the apparent desire to get the mounting under-way, and the next stage of courtship begins.

Getting to the point where the two animals are in body contact, essentially having begun the consort, does not mean that they will automatically start mating. Sometimes they do, but this depends on the male. If the male is motivated to begin a copulation, he will usually reach out and place his hands on the sides of the females hips. This "hip touch" is his way of requesting that the female stand up on all fours—the position necessary for copulation to occur. But many times the male is not quite ready; in this case the female has her own repertoire of behaviours designed to get the mounting started. This third stage of active female courtship is characterised by the attempts of the female to start a mount series.

SERIES MOUNTING AND THE THIRD STAGE OF FEMALE COURTSHIP ❧

Two basic copulatory patterns are found in the primates: single mounting and series mounting. Single mounting species copulate with a single mount in which the male mounts the female, thrusts several times, ejaculates and dismounts. The copulation is complete. Series mounting is more complicated, and requires more sustained co-operation and co-ordination between the mating pair. In series mounting species, such as Japanese macaques, a copulation requires a series of mount-thrust-dismount sequences before ejaculation is achieved. The number of mounts prior to the ejaculatory mount varies between about five and 15, as does the number of thrusts within any mount. The copulating pair thus spends considerable amount of time sitting together in body contact, not doing anything, right in the middle of a copulation.

Getting a mount series started is sometimes up to the female, if the male does not show the initiative as described above. If the female has been sitting in body contact with the male for several minutes and nothing is happening, then she may begin to appear impatient; at this point, the nervousness and fearfulness of the earlier stages are gone. The female may try a number of movements to "prompt" the male. For example, she may simply jerk her body. This can be done in conjunction with an estrus hack, a bark like vocalisation heard only from estrous females. If the male fails to respond to these hints, the female may begin to manipulate an object on the ground, like a twig or a stone, turning it over and moving it around. Sometimes she will just swipe at the dirt or slap the ground. Because mounting is from behind, the animals do not sit face to face. The male is usually behind the female, either facing her back, or facing away. During these prompting behaviours she will be turning repeatedly to look at the male.

During one focal animal session with a female named Butch, I recorded that she was engaged in what appeared to be a consort with a particularly "slow to respond" male. All the behaviours described above were performed and repeated in varying sequence, to no avail. Butch then engaged in a purely manipulative interaction—she got to her feet and began to scream defensively at a nearby male, as though he had been threatening her, when he wasn't even looking at her. The ploy proved successful; the male with whom she was consorting jumped to his feet and mounted her, thus beginning the series. I assumed that is was important that the other animal was another adult male, a potential competitor to her consort partner, but I subsequently witnessed this behaviour on several occasions and the other animal was often a female, or even a juvenile.

When collecting focal animal data, the researcher records the identity of the animal with whom the subject is interacting. One column is used to record behaviour, another to indicate if the behaviour was directed by the subject animal or received by the subject animal, and a third to enter the identity of the other animal. While recording the behaviour of a female attempting to start a mount series, I might thus write down that the subject threatened—to animal X. If the preceding behaviours have been mount prompting behaviours, like ground slapping and body jerking, then it is obvious from the context that this was yet another mount prompting behaviour.

That the age and sex of the unwitting participant in these scenarios was not necessarily important became clear to me one day when the female I was watching, suddenly turned and started threatening in my direction. I had been watching her for over 30 minutes, and the last 10 minutes of which she had utilised trying to prompt the male to mount. I looked left and right wondering who the intended recipient of this bluff was; when I looked back, both the female and the male were threatening *me*. Again, this ploy was successful, as the male did begin mounting. Sheepishly, I entered "me" in the other animal column. Apparently neither age, sex, nor *species* was important in terms of the identity of the other animal. Later, I came to be quite familiar with this behaviour, thus adding a new behaviour to my ethogram which I called "threaten the observer".

The animals made use of the human observers in other contexts as well. Wild Eyes is a female well known to researchers at the site because of her bold personality and relative lack of fear of humans. As I was collecting data on her one day I noticed that she was going through some of the standard motions of a female in stage two of courtship, but I could not identify the male object of her affections. To my chagrin I realised that there was no male, and that these various "'follows" and "sit nears" and "inch closers" were being directed at me. It didn't help that she was particularly bold and quickly proceeded to the "sit in body contact" stage. Like all primatologists I had in mind the magical images of the first time that a chimp made body contact with Jane Goodall, or a gorilla reached out to touch the hand of Dian Fossey. But, having Wild Eyes sit herself in body contact with me under courtship circumstances was hardly magical. She went so far as to stretch out her hind leg and place her foot on my clipboard, covering up my data collection sheet. I had no hesitation in aborting the focal animal session and going off in search of another subject somewhere far away from Wild Eyes.

Body jerking, estrus hacking, manipulating objects, slapping the ground, and threatening an innocent passerby do not complete the list of things that a female can do to try to prompt a male to perform a mount series. A very obvious signal, normally employed only after the above tactics have failed, is the sexual presentation. The female assumes the correct standing posture for mounting, thereby presenting her hindquarters to the male. This is hard for a male to ignore, although some do. Faced with this kind of desperate situation, a female uses the ultimate weapon of courtship communication: that of attempting to mount *him*.

Why this slowness or reluctance on the part of the male? The above is, after all, a common occurrence. Yet sexual selection theory and cultural bias lead us to expect that males should not be reluctant or choosy, but aggressive—taking advantage of all reproductive opportunities. Usually once a male has permitted a female to sit in body contact with him he is committed to the consort, so it is not a case of male choice. If he didn't want that female, he would not have let her sit in body contact with him. The male may simply be distracted, unable to focus on the copulation at hand, or he may be somehow physically not ready. Eventually he *is* ready, however, and a mount series begins.

**An estrous female screams defensively in the direction
of a male who has just chased her into a water hole**

STAGE FOUR OF FEMALE COURTSHIP ❧

The fourth stage of female courtship is attempting to maintain a mount series. Within the mount series this same list of behaviours may be exhibited by the female when trying to prompt the male to mount again. Jeff Bullard focussed his research on this prompting behaviour of the females within a mount series.[24] He found evidence that the females were trying to maintain a certain timing between the mounts in the series and suggested that this timing was physiologically important for the female.

The mount series ends with the ejaculatory mount. After a number of thrusts, the male will suddenly become rigid in posture and stare off into the distance for several seconds. At this time, the female also shows characteristic behaviours e.g. turning to look back at the male, which she usually has not done up to now during any mounts. Often, she will also reach back with her hand, thus supporting his full weight on her remaining three legs (his hind feet are clasped around her hind legs in what is called the double-foot-clasp mount); with this hand she will grab the fur of his face, neck, or head, and pull him toward her. The male then dismounts and the two animals separate and sit a few meters apart. If this was the first mount series of the consort, then this couple will likely stay together for a few days, engaging in copulations a number of times throughout the day. The animals do not spend the entire day copulating. In fact, the majority of their time is spent in regular activities such as travelling and foraging, although the consorting pair are doing these things together. Once the consort is well under way, (that is, after at least one copulation has been completed), the two animals give the impression of being mutually bonded, of mutually co-operating in the consort bond. It is the female mount prompting behaviours which tend to give the impression of her being more interested and motivated than the male.

Males are not always as resistant to the advances of females during mating season as this detailed description of female courtship might suggest. Sometimes the male appears to be equally interested in the consort; then the two animals are able to establish a consort bond very quickly, including regular mount series. In these cases, however, the various behaviours which make up the courtship repertoire may go unseen. Courtship in Japanese monkeys is highly variable, not stereotyped and ritualised. Although a repertoire of behaviours exists, it will not necessarily be displayed in the formation of every consort bond.

---

24 For further reference see: Bullard, J. 1984. Mount prompting behaviors of female Japanese macaques (*Macaca fuscata*). M.A. thesis, Dept. of Anthropology, The University of Alberta, Edmonton, Canada.

MALE COURTSHIP ❧

Males are not always passive recipients of female advances, and are often motivated to engage in mating behaviour. The initiators of many consort pairings, they too have a repertoire of courtship behaviours. Like female courtship, male courtship can be categorised in four stages: first, long distance advertising; second, attempting to gain the attention of, and proximity to, a specific female; third, attempting to attain body contact; and fourth, beginning a mount series.[25]

The most obvious long distance attention getting behaviour performed by male Japanese macaques during mating season is the "demo" or "display", a technique generally believed to be the male's way of drawing the attention of estrous females. He will climb onto a structure, preferably one that is not too rigid, and use his whole body to vigorously shake it. Sometimes loud, aggressive vocalisations will accompany the shaking. This behaviour is noticeable at a distance, and gains the attention of females. Within the enclosure at the site in Texas, few tall trees can be used for these displays, but the animals make use of artificial structures such as metal towers for this purpose. During mating season, it is also common to see and/or hear a peripheral male, in the trees outside the enclosure, giving a noticeable branch shaking display.

Whether the male has a specific female in mind when making this display is not known, for this display behaviour is too far away to be considered a communication intended for a specific recipient. It is in the next stage of courtship that the male is clearly directing his behaviour toward one specific female, to try to get her to accept his sitting nearby. From the behaviours displayed by the male, the female would certainly know that he is interested in forming a consort, not in entering into a nonsexual grooming bout. These behaviours include "strutting," "bird dogging," and something that has been called a "whirl-pivot." A male displaying these courtship behaviours is not easy to miss. These behaviours are obvious and unlike the behaviours shown by males at other times of the year.

Strutting is as it sounds. A male will walk by a female with his tail flipped up on to his back, walking with an exaggerated placement of the feet and swagger of the shoulders. Often he will turn to stare directly at the female, this stare sometimes accompanied by a lip quiver. The lip quiver is a gesture in which the lips are pursed or puckered, and then quivered. It resembles a kissing gesture in humans, one that might be given across a room.

The "bird dog" begins much like a strut, but is more obvious. Here the male will first approach the female in the strutting manner, then suddenly turn and begin to trot away. The trot is an unusual gait for males, again very exaggerated, with high stepping feet and not much speed. He will then suddenly

---

25 This categorisation of male courtship behaviour was provided to me, in part by Linda Fedigan who has spent more time observing the mating behaviour of males.

stop and freeze in position, with one leg bent and off the ground, and with face and chin jutting forward. At this point a male looks very much like a bird dog on a hunting trip; hence the name.

The whirl-pivot, again directed at a specific female, shares some of the elements of strutting and bird dogging. In a whirl-pivot the male will approach the female in the strutting manner, stop close to her, stare into her eyes and lip quiver, then abruptly wheel around on one leg so that his hindquarters are only a short distance from her face. This is an elaborate behaviour to tempt or lure the female into entering into a consort.

These behaviours appear to be designed to entice rather than to frighten the females. The lip quiver is occasionally seen in the non-mating context, and it is generally believed to be a gesture of appeasement or reassurance. Nonetheless, the behaviour of some females suggests that they are apprehensive. In both this stage, and the next, where the male will actually attempt to touch the female, sit down in body contact with her, or even mount her, she may run or walk away. If the female does stay, she may frequently direct fear grimaces to the male. This is a major difference between male and female courtship. Both the female initiative (proceptive) behaviours described above, as well as the more passive acceptance of male sexual advances (receptive behaviours) show evidence of fear, even for high ranking females. Male courtship behaviours are characterised by no such fear and caution. While it is common to see females fear grimacing, I have never seen a male fear grimace in a courtship context. This is understandable, because it is the males who are larger bonds and stronger, and who show high levels of aggression to females during mating season. Males need not fear becoming the object of an aggressive attack from an estrous female who is trying to court him, or from one who is accepting courtship advances from him.

In the third stage, as the male attempts to gain body contact with the female, he will employ behaviours very different from those a female uses at a similar stage. After the strutting and bird dogging and whirl pivoting, and, if the female is still there,[26] the male may gain body contact by simply walking up and placing his hand on her back. Rocky was famous for placing his hand under the female's chin while peering into her eyes, but this was not observed in other males. While females seemed to accept the idea that some time will pass between making body contact and attempting to get a mount series started, for the males, these two stages might be collapsed into one. This will happen when the first actual physical contact that the male makes with the female is in the form of a hip touch, which is her cue to stand up and assume the mounting posture. If a female has stayed around for all the advances up until now, it would not be uncommon for her to respond positively to this hip touch, and thus mounting may begin with the first body contact. If she does not, the pair may

---

26 Females do often walk out on these performances, as Linda Fedigan comments in Primate Paradigms, or, if the male is very high ranking, she may crouch when touched and fail to respond. See her chapter on Sociosexual Behavior under Consort Bonds, 1992. Chicago: University of Chicago Press.

sit in body contact for a short time; then the male will again try the hip touch to get the female to stand for mounting. I have seen cases of a female indicating lack of interest by lying down in response to the male's touch. But by this stage the male is likely to persist. A female who lies down or who refuses to stand up in response to the hip touch may find the male literally trying to pull her to her feet. This could end with the departure of the female or with the beginning of a mount series.

I have not included a fifth stage of male courtship—attempting to maintain a mount series—because for the most part, if the male initiates a mount series and the female is co-operative, he will not have to work to maintain the regular mounting. In fact I have witnessed courtship advances by males which culminated in a mount series beginning; then the female ends up displaying mount prompting behaviours to keep things going.

In the descriptions of male and female courtship presented here, one sex or the other is depicted as the active player from beginning to end, with the other as the passive acceptor or rejector of the advances. Often these two roles are differentiated. However, there are relationships in which the establishment of the consort bond is less straightforward, and the pair of animals may take turns being the pursuer and pursuee. It may take them a long time to get it together, if they ever do. Not all courtship ends in consort.

AGGRESSION IN THE MATING SEASON ❧

Chasing behaviour of males toward females increases dramatically during mating season. This is clearly related to courtship and/or mating, yet it is not easy to place this in the courtship categorisation presented above. This chasing behaviour is quite variable, ranging from a bouncy, stylised chase which does not seem to be particularly aggressive and in which the chaser does not appear to want to catch the female, to very serious, very real chases with accompanying aggressive vocalisations, in which the male may pin and viciously bite the female, sometimes inflicting mortal wounds. Possibly there are different explanations for the "courtship chases" as opposed to the "aggressive chases". Both increase dramatically in mating season, and exactly how they figure in the formation of consort pairs is not known.

My impression has always been that females try to get away, and stay away, from these chasing males. Linda Fedigan, who has studied the Arashiyama West monkeys in Texas, has not seen any evidence that females respond positively to this kind of behaviour on the part of the males.[27] However we are left with the question of how this behaviour could have evolved to this point if it were having a negative effect on the male's reproductive success. Recently,

---

27 Linda Fedigan, personal communication.

Barbara Smuts suggested that male coercion may be a factor in sexual selection—that females may submit to matings with males out of fear of further aggression from them.[28] In discussing this question with Lou, I was reminded that some of the central males who were regularly engaged in the bouncy courtship chases were rarely if ever seen mating, while some of the younger adult males of the peripheral troop would run into the troop, chasing different estrous females, and later be seen consorting. Apparently, some kinds of chases work for some of the males some of the time, but there is much that we do not yet understand about the role of male chasing and male aggression during the mating season.

An increase in aggression is one major mating-season activity. Courtship chasing is an important example, with females responding as though all chases are dangerous. Wounds and injuries, particularly to females, increase noticeably during mating-season. Early primatologists believed that the male-female sexual bond was paramount in holding societies together. We now know that this is not the case; social life is continuous, and sexual behaviour periodic. Furthermore, those who observe the often disruptive mating season interactions cannot help but dispute that sexual bonding holds the group together. One longtime researcher of the Arashiyama West monkeys commented that social life appeared to persist *in spite of* the sexual interactions of adult males and females, and certainly not *because of* them.

SAME-SEX SEXUAL INTERACTIONS ✌

Female-female consorts are not uncommon in the Arashiyama West Colony of Japanese macaques. I hesitate to call this homosexual behaviour because, in current North American usage, this implies a lifetime orientation of an individual. The vast majority of any female's sexual interactions will be with males, although female-female consorts appear to be part of the normal repertoire of female behaviour. Only one female is known from the Arashiyama West colony who exclusively consorted with same-sex others and never reproduced.

Female-female consorts involve the same intense bond as do male-female consorts. A consorting female pair would not be confused with a pair of females engaging in the typical kin based female-female social interactions. A consorting pair of females are distinct in their behaviour: they tend to be hyperactive and noisy, engaging in regular estrus vocalisations. In some ways they seem to be more intensely involved with one another than do animals in a male-female consort. It is not uncommon for the members of a female-female consort to

---

28 Smuts, Barbara B. and Robert W. Smuts.1993. Male aggression and sexual coercion of females in nonhuman primates and other mammals: Evidence and other theoretical implications. Advances In The Study Of Behavior. 22:1-61. Academic Press.

threaten an observer and generally to act in a manner reminiscent of possessive behaviour in humans.

Female-female consorts can involve females of any age and of any rank. Power asymmetry is not a noticeable aspect of the relationship—the interactions do not resemble dominance interactions. Like male-female consorts, the bond between the two females seems to be based primarily on a sexual attraction, but also implicates many other behaviours. The pair may stay together for days or even weeks, travelling, sleeping, and eating together. One of the major differences between a female-female consort and a male-female consort is the absence of sexual behaviour organised into the series mount form of copulation. The females do mount one another and the mounter will rub her genital region on the back of the mountee, but these mounts are irregularly spaced and the animals alternate roles. The two females do not simulate the mount series pattern that leads to ejaculation of the male in a male-female consort.

I have been asked by students how the other animals react or respond to these female-female consorts. I have never collected data specifically on these same-sex consorts, or the behaviour of others toward them, but my impression is that the others do not react at all, and that they are no more or less interested in a female-female consort than they are in a male-female consort. However, a female-female consort is vulnerable to attacks and chases by males more than is a male-female consort.

INBREEDING AVOIDANCE ☙

Primatologists are interested in the question of what animals are chosen as mates by others, or which are the most successful at competing for mates. That is, we want to know who tends to mate with whom. For example, there has always been the assumption that higher ranking males had greater mating and reproductive success, as was discussed in Chapter Three. We have found very little in terms of a clear pattern of which animals get to mate, and which do not. In the large Arashiyama West Colony of Japanese macaques, no class of animals is excluded from mating: high and low ranking animals mate; old and young adults (and even sub-adults) mate; central and peripheral animals mate. There are no clear patterns of mating preference, with one striking exception. Like the vast majority of primate populations for which this information is available, these animals tend not to mate with close maternal relatives. Brother-sister and mother-son matings are virtually nonexistent, and even matings between less closely related individuals are uncommon. Familiarity in early life probably explains the reduced sexual attraction between these maternally related individuals. It is likely that inbreeding does occur between animals related paternally. For example, Rocky and Midori are not related through maternal lines, but for all we know, and for all they know, they could have the same father. We have no evidence that they have any knowledge or recognition of paternity.

8

The Future of the South Texas Snow Monkey

Linda Fedigan of the University of Alberta introduced me to the Arashiyama West snow monkeys in 1981. Her involvement with the troop began when they were first transported to North America in 1972. She continues to be involved with the colony today, helping to maintain the monkey database, sending money, and making biannual visits to the site. We have made several trips to the site to meet with Lou and see the monkeys and discuss the ongoing problems of colony management. On one occasion Linda and Lou and I sat on a hill overlooking the waterhole quietly watching the monkeys around us. Linda interrupted the silence with the comment that it always amused her to think about how the monkeys carry on living their lives day to day, happily oblivious to the tremendous problems faced by the humans who seek to protect this life for them. The focus of this book has been on the social life of the monkeys, and I now turn to a brief discussion of the monumental problems faced by the protectors and managers of the colony.

During the 1970's, while the troop was under the care of the family of Edward and Clementina Dryden of Encinal, Texas, the family assumed responsiblity for all expenses associated with maintaining the group. They paid the salary of one on-site manager, usually a graduate student who was able to use the opportunity to conduct behavioural research on the monkeys. The search for a new home for the colony was underway shortly after Edward Dryden's death in 1974. Dr. Claud Bramblett of the University of Texas was actively involved in this process and it was ultimately one of his students, Lou Griffin, who secured the new home near Dilley. A non-profit organization called the Arashiyama West Institute was formed. This nonprofit organization would assume financial responsibility for the animals, funding the daily maintenance and manager's salary through research grants.

The monkeys were moved to the site near Dilley, their current home, in the summer of 1980. Sabre Noyes, the last manager to work for the Drydens in Encinal and the first to work for the Arashiyama West Institute in Dilley toiled for the better part of two years trying to move the monkeys. Although a large group of monkeys was captured and moved by a volunteer team in July of 1980, the entire move—from the first capture at Encinal to the last release at Dilley—took much longer. Lou Griffin, then a graduate student at the University of Texas, took over the job of on-site manager in Dilley when Sabre Noyes left. It was intended that she would follow in the tradition of Encinal and collect

111

behavioral data for her dissertation while acting as manager. It quickly became apparent, however, that funding would not be available as had been hoped. Over the next few years Lou Griffin came to assume almost the entire responsibility, to be the sole caregiver and fundraiser for the colony.

For scientific purposes, the value of the colony has always been in the wealth of background data available on all individuals in the group, dating back to the early 1950's. Individual identification, exact age, and maternal kinship relationships are known, in addition to extensive life history information on troop members. This, combined with the semi-free ranging status, the safe location, the accessibility of the animals, and the ease of observation renders the group ideal for certain kinds of behavioral research. For most of the time that the colony has been in North America, the raison d'etre of the colony and the primary mandate in its management, has been the research program.

Increasingly, however, this research mandate has come to share time with a different but not incompatible mandate, that of a sanctuary whose goal is to preserve and protect the animals as valuable in their own right, not just as tools for human research interests. There are several reasons for the development of this dual identity, which is reflected in the current and somewhat cumbersome official name of the organization: The South Texas Primate Observatory: Arashiyama West Snow Monkey Sanctuary.

One factor in the development of this dual identity was funding. Throughout the 1980's it became increasingly clear that funding from research sources would not be forthcoming. This was partly due to the fact that the colony was being maintained for a certain kind of research—observation of the social and ecological behavior of a naturally occuring and semi-free ranging population—which was not the invasive biomedical or highly controlled experimental research with direct human application which was easier to sell. Through media exposure the colony came to be known to individuals and groups who are primarily interested in animal welfare, and small amounts of money began to trickle in from these sources. Kay McMichael Trevino provided an important connection to this community and has worked tirelessly on behalf of the monkeys for the past several years. While this funding source has never been enough to provide financial stability, it did represent more money than came in from research related sources. Accepting money from individuals and groups with an animal welfare mandate meant that the sanctuary status would have to be protected should it come into conflict with research objectives or management operations.

The first and best example of change after animal welfare people started to give money had to do with the sale of animals to zoos or other research facilities. Until 1986, small numbers of animals were sold to zoos and noninvasive research projects. The population was steadily growing, and the financial situation was desperate. Many of us argued to Lou that if the sale of surplus animals could provide some regular income which would provide some security for the troop as a whole, then it was not only worth it, but that it was unavoidable. The argument is fine, of course, until the time comes to decide which animals will be captured, taken from their families and their freedom, packed in a small traveling kennel and dropped off at an airport loading dock. The terror in the animals' eyes and the sense of betrayal as a protector and caregiver are overwhelming. Being forced to sell some animals in order to try to ensure some security for the others was among the most difficult things that Lou, as manager, ever had to do. When it became clear that accepting money from animal welfare sources would mean an end to the sale of animals, Lou was frankly delighted to oblige. Even the small amounts of money that come from animal welfare sources is more than the trickle that was generated by animal sales. Regarding the animals as valuable in their own right, whose well being needed to be protected above all else, has never posed any ideological problems for Lou Griffin, who has always had great respect for the rights of other animals. She also believes deeply in the value of what can be learned from observing these animals, and thus sees protecting them in their own right while simultaneously making them available for observational research projects as perfectly compatible.

The dual identity does pose some problems however, as it is difficult to 'serve two masters'. To some in the animal welfare movement the very word research provokes a knee jerk reaction based on the assumption that any and all use of animals is wrong. Sometimes those with this perspective have a narrow view of what research entails, a view that is dominated by images of monkeys in restraining chairs. Those in the scientific community, on the other hand, can have a similar reaction to the mere mention of animal rights, based again on a narrow view of a broad perspective, and often based on dealings with the more militant factors in the movement. Since the mandate of the South Texas Primate Observatory is to protect and preserve the animals in their own right, and to keep them available for valuable observational research, objectives that are compatible, it is disheartening to face the dismissive reactions of some members of both communities. One well known animal rights organization tried to discredit the Observatory in the animal welfare community by 'uncovering' and 'exposing' the fact that animals had been sold in the past to research facilities. The fact that a multimillion dollar organization would try to financially destroy a small and sometimes desperate operation which houses primates living in conditions which captive animals anywhere would envy, conditions which are what such organizations are purportedly trying to secure for animals every- where, is very distressing. Likewise, in the scientific community it is sometimes assumed that since the colony is presented as a snow monkey sanctuary, it cannot be preserving its status as a research facility, but this is less common.

The problems with preserving the Observatory as a research facility derive from the lack of money and personnel to handle the maintenance of the data base. With the large size of the population and the tradition of maintaining daily records, this is a full time job in itself. One person should be available at all times to conduct a daily census and to update the data files. Without a trapping facility, the system of individual tattoos has come to be imperfect over the years, with a few animals making it to adulthood without a tattoo. Lou of course knows the individuals, tattooed or not, but is unable to commit her time to this plum job of watching monkeys every day. She is also responsible for fundraising, feeding, purchasing supplies, office paperwork, database paperwork, supervision of onsite researchers, transport of persons and animals, arranging veterinary care, caring for sick animals, trapping and tattooing, site repairs, truck repairs . . . and so on. Temporary onsite researchers are a potential source of assistance, but as often as not the studies are of short duration and the individual student becomes experienced enough to be really helpful at about the same time that he or she is scheduled to leave.

While at one level we can point to the size of the group as evidence that they are thriving in this environment, the great increase in the size of the population is itself a major threat to the security of the colony as a whole, whether it be as a sanctuary for monkeys or a research facility. There are now well over 500 animals in the group, which puts intense pressure on the local habitat, makes database maintenance increasingly difficult, and may alter social life. This is a very thorny problem, one which has yet to be solved. The food enhanced environment is the cause of the population increase, but reducing food supplies significantly is not a solution because this results in the animals roaming further and further away from the site, something they were never intended to do. The difficulty in trapping animals is part of the problem with any contraceptive system we might use. In 1988 and 1989, hundreds of hours of labor and thousands of dollars were spent experimenting with Depo provera, a long acting injectable contraceptive for females. For many reasons, this resulted in no significant decrease in the size of the birth cohort. We are currently considering a proposal for a population control project involving the substance gossopol which would be administered to males, but again we face enormous logistical problems in seeing this project through to the point where we would see a significant decrease in a birth cohort.

It is now at the point where drastic measures are being considered, such as vasectomies and tubal ligations of large numbers of animals. Socially it would be best not to interefere with female reproduction, but this may be unavoidable. Nonreproducing animals would of course no longer be suitable for certain kinds of research, and this is a something we may have to live with. Knowing what you, the reader, now know about the importance of family for these animals, imagine the difficulty of deciding which females will never have any more offspring. Even getting past the difficulties in deciding to pursue this course of action, there is still the problem of the time, money, and expertise that would be required of such a project, none of which are currently available.

It is possible that either an animal welfare organization or a scientific funding agency would provide a grant for a special project such as massive population control. Grants for specific, tangible items or projects are, while not readily available, easier to come by than are funds for daily maintenance. Nobody, it seems, wants to pay for monkey chow, truck repairs, and salaries. So how does the facility survive day to day, month to month?

The number one benefactor since 1979 has been Mrs. Patricia Daley who owns the section of the Burns Ranch on which the facility is located. In addition to providing the monkeys with a home, Mrs. Daley and some of her family have provided ongoing financial and emotional support. A number of animal welfare organizations have also given lump sums of several thousand dollars now and again. We have Shirley McGreal, founder of the International Primate Protection Leage and a powerful and controversial figure in both the animal welfare and scientific communities, to thank for promoting the Observatory whenever and wherever she can. She has said that the monkeys of Arashiyama have the best living conditions of any group of primates in North America, and she would know. A biannual newsletter generates small sums of money from a number of individual donations. Thus the Observatory operates on a shoe string budget with no reliable income and with the constant worry of where the money for next months bills will come from. These bills include payment on the land which will be the future home for the colony, and they exceed $7000.00 per month.

Oddly enough, the physical, social, and psychological health of the colony has interfered with fundraising in some circles. The animals are not pathetic at all, and thus don't seem to have the ability to tug at the heart strings of those in a position to provide them with financial stability and security. It is much easier to get money to rescue a single pitiful animal from a bad situation than it is to guarantee the health of a large healthy colony. What the Observatory needs is a large endowment which would generate a regular income thus freeing up much needed time and energy to address problems such as over population.

One very positive development in terms of the future of the colony was the recent acquisition of a 75 hectare tract of land which will become the new home for the colony. For several years there has been pressure to move the

While on a field study course from the University of Calgary, Elizabeth Scott tries to get a look at a new baby hidden in the lap of an adult female.

animals, primarily because the current home has been denuded by the troop. It provides little in the way of natural flora or cover, and the animals are tending to range further and further from the site. The new site is located 16 kilometres from Dilley, and unlike the current site, much of it is dense brush. A new fence has been designed which is intended to be truly monkey-proof and a 2 hectare proto-type has been built which will be used to house the splinter troop, some peripheral males, and the vervets on a temporary basis. This 2 hectare enclosure will provide the opportunity to to assess the success of the new design—that is to see if any monkeys can get out. If the design proves successful, an area of 32 hectares of dense brush containing a large creek, two water holes, and two small areas of cleared fields will be fenced off as the home for the main troop.

A third function of the observatory is an educational one. One and two day field schools are run from some local universities and colleges, and the University of Calgary conducts an annual 30 day field training school. This 30 day field school is very successful because of the unique educational opportunity it provides to students. Nowhere else on this continent could students be given the opportunity to study wild primates roaming essentially free. As wild populations in third world countries rapidly diminish, and as political circumstances become increasingly unstable, opportunities for this kind of educational experience disappear. The South Texas Primate Observatory offers reasonable expense and the safety and stability of the United States.

The dedicated efforts of a small number of people have safegaurded and preserved this colony for education, observational research, and for the welfare of the animals themselves for almost a decade and a half. But as costs rise and stable financial support remains elusive, there is no certainty that the colony will survive the next decade.

INDEX